SOME OF THE MANY QUESTION FOR YOU IN DETAIL

Do **Saxon**® math books still offer an excellent math curriculum?

Used vs. new textbooks?

Do I need to buy the new editions?

How do I record academic credits?

How do I transcript the high school courses?

Calculator or no calculator? When to use one?

Expensive graphing calculator vs. the inexpensive scientific calculator -- which is better?

Follow the order of Math 54, 65, 76, 87. . . . Or skip a book?

What are the similarities and differences between Math 87 and Algebra 1/2?

Is the edition of the book Important?

Must the student have calculus in high school to study engineering at the university?

What does needing a tutor signify?

Do I really need to pay $50 to $100 for a CD, DVD or video tutorial?

www.homeschoolwithsaxon.com

Grades 4-12

Using

JOHN SAXON'S MATH BOOKS

How homeschool parents can successfully use them – and save money!

ART REED

AJ PUBLISHERS

Using John Saxon's Math Books

AJ Publishers, LLC
117 N. Washington
Enid, OK 73701-4019

Second Printing 2009, © 2007 by AJ Publishers, LLC

Printed in the United States of America

ISBN-13: 978-0-9792521-0-5

ISBN-10:   0-9792521-0-5

Library of Congress Catalog Number: 2007900062

Credits:
Cover by Amber Sutton, Enid, Oklahoma
Photo by Lynn Smith Portraits, Enid, Oklahoma
Website Design by www.BringTheBling.com, Vero Beach, Florida.

Reach us via the Internet

www.homeschoolwithsaxon.com

CONTENTS

Contents

Dedication Page

I dedicate this book to the memory of my mother. She impressed upon my brothers, sisters and me the importance of honesty and integrity. And she told us that wherever we went, she wanted us always to question *ignorance*!

Acknowledgements

It is well known that mathematicians and engineers are not the best writers in the world, which is why I am greatly indebted to two English majors: my wife Judy and her sister, Elizabeth "Lish" Glasser. I deeply appreciate their advice – sometimes threats – ensuring that, among other dumb mistakes, I did not put phrases in *"quotations, italics and bold print,"* all at the same time! I am equally indebted to Professor (Retired) Frederic P. Lamb for his ideas and recommendations.

I am also most appreciative of the advice and assistance given me by my former colleague and fellow mathematician, John Matousek, and to Allison McCune Davis, a family friend and homeschool parent of three.

Last, I want to thank the hundreds of homeschool parents and students, teachers and school administrators, who inspired and encouraged me to write this book. I trust I have accomplished what they asked me to do.

Foreword

While I was associated with Saxon Publishers in Norman, Oklahoma, the elementary school teachers there would remind me that, while I could easily find the rate of change of the volume of an expanding object, I was not smart enough to answer questions about the K-3 math textbooks. This book, then, is about the proper selection and successful use of John Saxon's math books from *Math 54* through *Calculus* and *Physics.*

During the past nine years of advising and assisting homeschool parents about curriculum choices for their children, I noticed many of their calls to me were the result of having received inaccurate or inadequate – sometimes downright erroneous – advice.

This erroneous advice came from other homeschool parents, discussion groups, well-meaning but uninformed or inexperienced publishing company employees, or from inexperienced employees of homeschool textbook distributors.

I wrote this book to answer those questions that today still confront homeschool parents using John Saxon's math books. After reading this book, you may still have a question or two that were not completely answered within its covers. Every child is different! What may work with the vast majority of homeschool students may need to be changed or adapted for an individual child.

For that reason, original purchasers of this book have the opportunity to subscribe to the on-line advisory *Homeschool Newsletter* at **www. homeschoolwithsaxon.com.** The site contains updated purchasing recommendations, information on printing errors, and professional advice, as well as links to educational support materials, to assist homeschool parents and students.

A brief comment or two about the four chapters dealing with Math 54, Math 65, Math 76 and Math 87.

If the readers read all four of these chapters in a single sitting, they will encounter quite a bit of repetitiveness.

The reason for this repetition is that the author assumes the readers will read the first twelve chapters and then focus on the level of the one specific textbook in which they are interested. They then will read just that additional chapter to acquire the needed information regarding that level book.

The author did not assume the reader would read all four chapters in one sitting. Before reading a specific chapter dealing with *Math 54, Math 65, Math 76,* or *Math 87,* please read the contents of pages one through fifty-two.

To avoid confusion, whenever the reader encounters book titles of *Math 54, Math 65, Math 76, Math 87, Algebra ½, Algebra 1, Algebra 2, Advanced Mathematics, Calculus,* and *Physics,* the reference is to one of John Saxon's math books. Using *algebra one* or *algebra two,* etc. refers to any such course using some other math textbook.

Saxon® was registered as a trademark of Harcourt Achieve, Inc. in August of 2006.

Definitions

*NOTE: Unusual words, titles or phrases that first appear in **bold italics** in the book are defined here to assist the reader. The reader may want to review the next several pages of definitions before continuing.*

Answer Key: The title used by the Homeschool Division of **Saxon®** to describe a softcover booklet that comes with the new third edition of *Algebra 2*, and the new second edition of *Calculus*. The booklet contains answers to problems in the textbook. This replaces what used to be called the *Home Study Packet*. It now includes the answers to the practice problems as well. It does not contain solutions to the problems or answers to test questions.

Automaticity: A process defined and described in the 1930's by Dr. Benjamin Bloom of the University of Chicago. It is the ability of the human brain to perform two tasks simultaneously, as long as one of the tasks has been over learned. It is acquired through repetition over an extended period of time.

Complete Package: A new term created by the marketing staff of Harcourt Achieve to describe what Saxon Publishers and homeschool parents previously referred to as the *Homeschool Kit*. The specific contents of each individual book's *Complete Package* will be described in the chapter on that particular textbook.

Holes in Mathematics: A description of what occurs in mathematics when students move forward in a series of math courses without mastering the basic material from earlier courses. Holes, or non-mastery of the material, develop; and as the student progresses, these holes become bigger and more difficult to fix.

Homeschool Testing Book: A softcover booklet that comes with the new third edition of *Algebra 2* and the new second edition of *Calculus*. It has the test forms and the step-by-step solutions to the test questions. This booklet was formerly titled *Test Forms*.

Homeschool Kit: A Homeschool Kit contains three separate items. They are (1) the **Student Textbook**, (2) a **Home Study Packet,** later titled **Homeschool Packet,** and (3) a **Test Forms Booklet**. The specific contents of each will be described in the chapter on that textbook.

Homeschool Packet: This packet consists of items (2) and (3) found in the Homeschool Kit described above. There is no textbook included in this packet. Test booklets can be purchased separately for about twelve dollars. <u>Home Study or Homeschool Packets are sold only with an accompanying Test Forms booklet.</u>

Incremental Development: John Saxon's original idea of introducing a small element or increment of a particular concept so that the student can practice that increment over a period of time before the next part is introduced.

Lesson Reference Numbers (LRN): In the newer editions of Saxon math textbooks, there is a small number in parenthesis under each of the numbered problems. The LRN indicates the original lesson in the book (in some cases more than one lesson) where the concept of that problem is first introduced.

Lesser Inclusive Credit: Because of the cumulative nature of his textbooks, every one of John Saxon's textbooks contains the basics of a less challenging course. For example, a student completing *Physics* (which is an Engineering Physics text) with a test average of C would certainly have done better had he taken *Introduction to Physics* first. He would have mastered the terminology and procedures, and when taking the more demanding *Physics* textbook, would have received a better grade. Thus the C in the more challenging *Physics* book would have resulted in an A or B in the less challenging *Introduction to Physics.* The same would hold true had he taken a *Basic Algebra* course before attempting the more rigorous *Algebra 1* textbook developed by John Saxon.

Lesser Included Grading Scale: The grading scale used to enable use of the lesser inclusive course or credit described above. If the regular grading scale for *Physics* was 90 = A, 80 = B, etc., then the lesser included grading scale for *Introduction to Physics* would be 75 = A, 65 = B, etc.

Long Term Memory: A part of the brain that retains information acquired and stored through repetition over an extended period of time. This is not the same as something "memorized" for a specific short-term use, like "cramming" the night before a test. It is, instead, a term often used to describe the process of "mastery."

Managing by Exception: A technique used by corporations that basically says to the managers not to micro-manage daily operations. The managers allow everything to function as long as all is working well. They keep their eyes open to deal with the exceptional problems as they arise. Like a good coach who doesn't correct the batter as he is swinging the bat in a ball game, but waits until the player returns to the dugout, a good manager avoids correcting every detail of the daily operations, waiting for a more appropriate and effective periodic review. In John Saxon's methodology, these observations would be the tests taken every four or five lessons.

News Releases: A link on the Saxon Homeschool Web site that provides up-to-date information about new books, changes in the series, etc. The link can be found on the left side of the Saxon Homeschool Web Site at *www.saxonhomeschool.com.*

Solutions Manual: A softcover manual that gives step-by-step solutions to the individual problems found in each lesson. Because of the simplicity of some problems, there may be just an answer. In the solutions manuals for the upper level math books, some interim steps in problems found in the latter lessons, which are assumed to have been mastered already, have been eliminated.

Test Forms Booklet: A softcover booklet containing the required tests and the test schedule. The Test Forms Booklet contains one copy of each of the required tests necessary to determine the student's mastery level. This booklet can be purchased as a separate item for about twelve dollars. The booklets for some editions may or may not contain step-by-step solutions to the test questions. Specifics for each book are contained in the separate chapters on each book.

John Saxon's Legacy

John Saxon was, among other things, a teacher, a leader, a graduate of West Point, and a great storyteller. I first met John and his wife Mary Esther in the late 1960's in my mother-in-law's kitchen in Enid, Oklahoma, while I was on leave preparing to go to Germany.

While his mother-in-law and mine had been members of the same sewing club and also the same Presbyterian Church for almost forty years, our military careers took us our separate ways, and I never had a chance to know him very well until I started teaching several years after he had already published his first algebra book in 1981.

That night in the kitchen, John told the story about when he flew the supply route from Japan to Korea – in between B-26 bombing runs – during the Korean War. He said he had not had much sleep in the preceding five days, and he was concerned that he would doze off while piloting the aircraft, so he instructed his enlisted crew chief to make sure he stayed awake.

"I told him that whatever it took, keep me awake! I woke up the next morning and I could barely move my right arm, the pain was so intense. I looked at my right shoulder and it was a dark purple color," John said. "I learned later that day that the crew chief kept punching my shoulder every time I started to doze off - all the way from Japan to Korea! I told him, Chief, you almost broke my shoulder. So he says to me, '**Kept you awake, Sir!**' "

The high school where I had done my student teaching had been using John's math books for several years. I liked using them, so when I started my first job as a high school math teacher, I asked for and received approval to buy his math books for two of my three math courses.

The first year I taught, I finished all the lessons in John Saxon's first *Algebra 2* books. When school was out, I drove to Norman to visit with John. When I bragged to him that we had finished his book, he smiled and, pitching me his new second edition, said, "Here. Try this new edition. It's seven lessons longer."

John and his finance officer loaded seventy of the new second edition *Algebra 2* books into the trunk of my car. As I drove home later that evening, I wondered what I would say to the highway patrolman if I were stopped and he looked in the trunk. John had given me the books, and I did not have a paid invoice for them.

I remember in the early days of his company, John had a personal policy that if a student found an error in one of his math books and wrote to him about it, John would send him five dollars for each error he found.

That fall, when we started using these brand new first printings of the new second edition of *Algebra 2*, one of my students found four problems with wrong answers.

I checked the answers and verified that the student was indeed correct. The four answers were wrong! The young man then asked about the twenty dollars that I had mentioned he would receive. So using my classroom telephone, I called John at his office.

I had placed the telephone on the speakerphone, so the class could hear the conversation. They appeared excited that they were actually sitting in their classroom, talking to the author and owner of the publishing company that had published their math book!

John asked me if I had verified that the answers were indeed in error, and I told him the student was correct, that the answers were in fact wrong. Without hesitation, John immediately asked the young man his name and congratulated him for finding them.

I reminded John about his "five dollar" policy. He agreed that the young man deserved the twenty dollars and that he should not have to wait around for the money. Then John, in a loud and clear voice said, **"Art, you pay him,"** and hung up! A warm summer evening in June and a free trunk load of seventy *Algebra 2* books flashed before my eyes as I gave the young man my only twenty-dollar bill.

John was both a mathematician and an engineer. After retiring from military service, while teaching mathematics at Rose State College in Oklahoma City, he was appalled to see that the incoming college students could not handle simple math concepts. So John decided to write his own math books to correct this.

I soon learned what John meant by "at-risk adults" when, some twenty years later, I also encountered college students who still did not understand fractions, percents or decimals. They were failing their basic algebra course at the local university where I taught mathematics.

Throughout John's years of publishing his math textbooks, he always used the words "students," "educators," and "responsibility" when speaking about his books. He had designed them to teach the basic concepts of mathematics. They were not designed to teach just "critical thinking" or "higher-order thinking" at the expense of this critical subject matter, as many books still do today to meet requirements of textbook selection committees.

One of John's favorite analogies of what was wrong with this idea was instances when he would tell his audience, most often teachers and administrators, "Understanding should **follow** doing, rather than **precede** it. If you're going to teach someone how to drive an automobile, don't lecture him on the theory of the internal-combustion engine. Get him to drive the car around the block."

John was always aware of and deeply concerned about our high school students as they continued to fall behind in their understanding of the basic concepts necessary to be successful in mathematics and science.

He believed so strongly in what he was doing that, in 1980, so that he could publish his first math book (an *Algebra 1* textbook), he borrowed money from his children, from his bank, mortgaged his house, and also borrowed against the value of his future military retirement pay!

More than twenty-five years later, we all know John and his company were a tremendous success! And we all know the legacy that John Saxon has left the field of mathematics – especially for homeschool families.

In July of 1993, in an open letter to then - President Clinton, John Saxon warned of the pending disaster in the areas of mathematics and science. He was concerned that educators were advocating teaching critical thinking when they should be teaching basic math concepts.

He complimented the President on the fact that, while still Governor of Arkansas, he had supported a bill in the Arkansas Legislature that returned control of textbook selection to the local school boards.

Local control was something John felt would keep the "unknowing" at the state level from being able to control the local school boards and administrators, and allow them to solve these problems locally.

John Saxon passed away on October 17, 1996. His children continued management of Saxon Publishers until it was finally sold to Harcourt Achieve in the fall of 2004.

I remember the summer day in 2004 when John Saxon's children announced the acquisition of Saxon Publishers by Harcourt Achieve at the Saxon Headquarters in Norman, Oklahoma.

Just a few minutes after the children had made their announcement, dark ominous clouds swept in, and in the midst of a torrential downpour, one of the biggest electrical storms in Norman's history knocked out all the electrical power and telephone lines to the Saxon Corporate headquarters after lightning had struck the building.

I told you John was a great storyteller. It appears, again, that he had the last word that day!

You Chose the Right Math Books

Congratulations on your choice of John Saxon's math books for your children. You have chosen the very best math textbooks on the market today. Although Saxon Publishers was acquired by Harcourt Achieve in 2004, the quality of the math content of John Saxon's math books has not changed.

Over the past several years I have received numerous calls from homeschool parents concerned that, because Saxon Publishers no longer existed, the quality of their books' content would diminish. Nothing could be further from the truth! While ownership has changed, the quality and integrity of the books' content still remain the same as when John Saxon was alive and guiding Saxon Publishers.

John Saxon's math series from kindergarten through high school is still the strongest and most comprehensive series of math books I have ever encountered. The books not only give students confidence in their ability to understand the necessary concepts of mathematics, but they teach students mastery of these concepts and not just how to memorize them to get a good test grade.

Perhaps even more important is the fact that, throughout my more than twelve years' experience in the classroom teaching with John Saxon's math books, I observed how his math series has helped all levels of math students: students who struggled with math, those who were average math students, and those who became National Merit Scholars.

I have kept in contact with many of my former students, hearing how well prepared they were for college math and science classes. And I have seen many of them advance into professions requiring strong math backgrounds.

What is it that makes John Saxon's math books so different and so unique? Why do his books work so well in a homeschool environment? Here are some of the reasons:

- They Challenge Stronger Students. The books are skill level and therefore, students can use higher level math books at a lower grade level if qualified to do so.

- They Assist Struggling Students. Students can easily take more time to master the material if needed, without losing mastery of material already covered.

- They Allow Mastery of Concepts. Through repetition over extended periods of time, the books foster mastery rather than memory of math concepts.

- They Use Incremental Development. The methodology of incremental development enables students to understand the entire concept much more easily by introducing smaller parts of a difficult math concept one at a time, rather than trying to teach the entire concept at once.

- They Involve Cumulative and Repetitive Concepts. Once the students are introduced to a particular math concept, they are continually and repeatedly asked to work with that concept throughout the remainder of the textbook.

- They Provide Flexibility. While it is not advisable to skip individual lessons or books, the textbooks provide parents with multiple options within the series of math books, from middle school through high school. These options assist the exceptional, as well as the struggling math student.

The individual applications and benefits of each of these will be explained in detail later in the book.

The books are easy to read and do an excellent job of challenging students. They are no-nonsense books that enable students to master the required concepts, allowing them to be successful in later math and science courses in high school, and at the college or university level.

This book is about how to successfully use John Saxon's math books from *Math 54* through *Calculus* and *Physics*. These suggestions will help improve the student's ability to be successful in mathematics, while helping their parents save money as well. John Saxon's math books were designed to be skill level books, to be taken in order from *Math 54* to *Calculus.* They are generally used by schools in the following order:

Math 54: A fourth grade math book. Sometimes used in fifth grade by students who did not receive a good math background in the fourth grade.

Math 65: A fifth grade math book. Sometimes used in the sixth grade by students who did not receive a good math background in the fifth grade.

Math 76: A sixth grade math book. Sometimes used in the seventh grade by students who did not receive a good math background in the sixth grade.

Math 87 and Algebra ½: Seventh grade pre-algebra books. Sometimes used in the eight and ninth grade by students who did not receive a good math background in the sixth or seventh grades.

Algebra 1: Used in either the seventh, eighth or ninth grade depending upon the student's math background. It is followed by *Algebra 2*, then *Advanced Mathematics* (a precalculus textbook). *Calculus* and *Physics,* then, follow *Advanced Mathematics.*

Mastery vs. Memory

When many parents attended math class in their high school days, their teacher would not always assign daily homework, and the book was organized so that multiple concepts were discussed in a single lesson with multiple lessons in each chapter.

These concepts or chapters were not always related to either the previous or the subsequent concepts or chapters. Students could pass chapter one, fail chapter two, and still have a passing grade. There was no cumulative structure to the book, nor were the concepts reviewed.

To overcome this deficiency, teachers would hand out review sheets just before the monthly or mid-term tests and assure students that if they could work these thirty or so review problems, they would easily pass the test in a few days.

So what did the students do? Naturally, they sought out a tutor or a fellow student to help them memorize those problems so they could pass the test. After cramming half the night before, or perhaps a couple of nights, they were ready for their test.

The test results under this review system usually resulted in anywhere from an A to a solid C, depending on the amount of extra credit offered by the teacher, because he was positive his students really knew what they were doing; they somehow just ended up with the wrong answer to several problems.

Ours is the only civilized and industrialized nation in the world that has our parents proudly announce, "Oh, I was never very good at math." No wonder! Educators taught students that memorizing for good test grades, not mastery of the material, was important.

In fact, educators still erroneously refer to this as learning! We are still using this method in most public and in some private schools today! John Saxon's math books, on the other hand, were designed to create mastery of the material, not memory.

Yes, tests remain critically important. Instead of a weekly review sheet giving the student the test questions to memorize, however, the student does the daily assigned work to master the requisite concepts that will be covered in the weekly test.

While every parent and student wants to receive one hundred percent on every test that is not essential. Minimal mastery of one of the tests occurs with a score of eighty (first time tested) in a fifty-minute test, with no partial credit. The answer is either all right or all wrong.

Mastery occurs through a process referred to as ***automaticity***. When John Saxon took his first manuscript to the University of Chicago, he asked Dr. Benjamin Bloom (of Bloom's Taxonomy) to look at his book's methodology. Dr. Bloom informed John that he had not created a new teaching method. He himself had come up with this concept in the early 1930's.

Dr. Bloom referred to this method as automaticity. He described this as the ability of the human mind to accomplish two things simultaneously so long as one of them was over-learned (or mastered). He told John that the two critical components of this phenomenon were *repetition* and *time.*

John was not familiar with the term automaticity, as described by Dr. Bloom. But while in the service, he had encountered military training techniques that used the concept of repetition over extended periods of time, and had found them very successful.

Automaticity is another way to describe the placing of information or data into our ***long term memory***. The process requires that the two components of repetition and of time, be used simultaneously.

10

Some time ago, I read an article about a world famous pianist who would practice his warm-ups at the piano each day while reading the newspaper! Since the news changed each day, I believe it is safe to assume that he had mastered his warm-ups!

It is this process in John Saxon's math books that creates the atmosphere for mastery of the material because they are used in conjunction with one another – repetition over extended time. Violating either one negates the process.

The experienced Saxon mathematics teacher does not grade the daily work, as that is only practice for the weekly test. Each day, the teacher checks to ensure that the student has done the required work, but he does not grade every single problem. Homeschool parents often ask me, "What do you mean you don't grade the daily work?"

I remind them that if they have a child taking piano lessons, hey do not sit on the piano bench with the student and watch every single piano key being struck. They listen from a distance and step in when they know something is amiss.

While we all would like the student to master the new concept on the day it is introduced, that does not happen with very many students. This is why there are only a few problems of the new concept the first day and each day thereafter, for several weeks, until mastery is achieved. Some homeschool parents, seeing their child is having trouble with the new concept, make the mistake of adding additional problems concerning that new concept, so the child can learn it more quickly.

Let me see if I understand this process. The student is having trouble doing the two new problems from the newly introduced concept, so we will give him ten more to have even more trouble with! Let's reverse the logic of that decision and see if this arrangement makes sense.

The student understands how to do the two new problems, so we add ten more of the same. Does that make sense? Why not let him do just those two problems today, two more tomorrow, and two more the next day, etc., for several more weeks? Why immediately increase his daily workload by thirty-three percent?

We will discuss John Saxon's methodology, and the pros and cons of saddling the student with additional review problems – and their repercussions – a little later in the chapter on *Using the Books Correctly*.

This same idea of monitoring the daily progress, but not becoming too deeply involved on a day-to-day basis, and allowing the weekly tests to reveal the problems the student has encountered is referred to in the corporate world, as **managing by exception.**

John Saxon's math books are the only math books I know of that test every Friday (every five lessons in *Math 54* to *Math 87)*. In his math books, the parent or teacher is only four to five days away from fixing any major problems that arise if the student does poorly on a weekly test.

In a single school year, the student using John Saxon's math books will have taken more than twenty tests. They are all cumulative tests, so there is little room for *memory* – only *mastery!*

What Editions to Use

Several years ago, I received a call from a homeschool parent who was concerned because her son was failing *Algebra ½* - and he was only on lesson 30! She mentioned to me that she had followed the advice of several of her homeschool group members, and had skipped *Math 87* because they had told her there was a lot of repetition.

I asked her what edition of *Math 76* she had used for her son; and she said it was an older *first edition.* No wonder he ran into difficulty! By 2005, that old edition of *Math 76* had been out-of-print for almost a decade.

I told her that I thought the problem was that the student had jumped into water over his head. While both the first and second editions of *Math 76* were excellent sixth grade textbooks in their day, changing testing requirements had rendered them inadequate sixth grade math books by 1997, when the new third edition was released.

She commented that it seemed very easy for her son to move from the second edition of *Math 65* to the first edition of *Math 76,* and I agreed with her. A student moving from the newer second or third edition of *Math 65* to the older first or second edition of *Math 76* would not be academically challenged.

Before I became aware of Saxon Publishers, I thought textbook publishers changed books every few years just to sell a new textbook, but that is not necessarily so.

Changing testing requirements, established by the federal government and the various individual states, require that textbook publishers upgrade their textbooks to ensure that the students using them meet these standards.

Not all new editions, however, are released solely because they are academically stronger textbooks. The new edition may not have been released because it contained an upgrade in conceptual materials. The publishers may have just added user conveniences such as *lesson reference numbers* or changed the cover of the book and order of the content, but not actually improved the academic content.

Over the years I have received thousands of email messages and telephone calls from homeschool parents whose children are experiencing difficulties in their mastery of mathematics; this problem generally occurs because the parents are using out-of-date, hand-me-down textbooks that are no longer up-to-date in their content.

Because the editions keep changing, it behooves the readers to keep abreast of the current editions of the math books to determine if they indeed have the correct textbook for the student. One does not necessarily need the newest and shiniest book, but the correct level math textbook, regardless of the edition.

I have also been asked what the differences are between the textbook that is used in the schools and the one that is sold to homeschool families.

As long as the editions are the same, whether the textbooks have a softcover or a hardcover, the contents of the schools' classroom textbooks are identical to the contents of the homeschool textbooks.

I recommend that parents with several children at home who will soon utilize *Math 54* through *Math 87* purchase the classroom hardbound edition of their textbook from the Saxon School Web site. They can then also purchase the other homeschool support materials (the solutions manual and the tests and worksheets manual) from the Saxon Homeschool Web site.

The Saxon Homeschool Web site is **www.saxonhomeschool.com.** Public and private schools use another Web site, which is **www. saxonpublishers.com.** While at the Saxon Homeschool Web site, make it a habit to look at the *news releases* for information on new editions or support materials. A direct link to these news releases will also be provided in my on-line advisory *Homeschool Newsletter* at **www.homeschoolwithsaxon.com.**

Unless the student has special needs, or the family is purchasing a hard cover middle grade textbook, the materials reflected on the Saxon School Web site are not needed.

The pros and cons of each edition's content will be discussed later in the section on that particular textbook. Listed here are the current 2007 editions of John Saxon's math books that I believe parents should still be using, whether the books are used or new.

Math 54, second edition or the new softcover third edition.

Math 65, second edition or the new softcover third edition.

Math 76, third edition or the new softcover fourth edition.

Math 87, second edition or the new softcover third edition.

Algebra ½, second or third edition.

Algebra 1, third edition.

Algebra 2, second or the new third edition.

Advanced Mathematics, second edition.

Calculus, first or the new second edition.

Physics, first edition.

Used vs. New Textbooks

There are three valid reasons why publishers release new editions of their math books. **First**, because mandated state or federal standards require them to revise the contents of their textbooks. **Second**, because they have developed new and useful technology that enhances the book's content. **Third**, they have voluntarily strengthened the contents of the book.

I would caution the reader, however, that not all textbook changes are made for such valid reasons. Knowing the content of the current edition of the math book, as well as that of the preceding edition, will therefore assist the reader in choosing whether to buy the new edition or stick with a used copy of the previous edition.

Over the past decade, I have observed that homeschool families with more than one child tend to keep the original textbooks and use them again for younger siblings, sometimes years later. There is nothing wrong with this practice unless the families have kept the books beyond their usefulness. Remember the homeschool parent who used the older, out-of-print, first edition of *Math 76?*

For example, I have a large, one hundred year old, two-inch thick book that contains tables of logarithmic and trigonometric functions. I also have an inexpensive, scientific calculator that contains all of that same data on a microchip inside the calculator.

The small, hand-held, scientific calculator now replaces the need for the cumbersome book of logarithmic and trigonometric tables – a rather expensive investment in its day.

If you are looking for some of the used math textbooks, make sure that all of the required support materials are there and that they match. With one or two exceptions, the support materials from one edition will not work with a different edition textbook.

When you go to a homeschool book fair and find some of John Saxon's used math books, or if you prefer to go on-line and find them, make sure you're buying a valid edition.

There are some simple guidelines to follow to ensure you are not buying history, but a valid, usable, used math book. **First**, unless the cover of the textbook has the edition printed on the outside of the cover immediately under the book's title, it is an older, out-of-print first edition textbook. Do not buy it!

All of John Saxon's usable textbook editions will have either *Second Edition* or *Third Edition* printed on the outside cover of the book, just under the book's title.

An exception to this rule would be the new softcover middle grade textbooks (*Math 54* through *Math 87*). These new softcover textbooks do not have the edition printed on the front cover but inside, on the copyright page.

Saxon Publishers, while still located in Norman, Oklahoma, started using the soft textbook covers to keep the cost of their **Homeschool Kit** down because they wanted to add a solutions manual without increasing the overall cost of the Kit.

Second, never buy a used first printing of any mathematics or physics textbook, as that is where the majority of the printing errors occur. In the newer editions, Saxon Publishers started using a manufacturing code, like 01S0104, which tells you that this is the first printing by Saxon Publishers in January of 2004.

You can find the code inside on the copyright page. Other forms of manufacturing codes will undoubtedly be used in future printings of textbooks. These manufacturing codes will be explained in the on-line advisory *Homeschool Newsletter* at www.homeschoolwithsaxon.com

Third, while some books do not require major updates, minor changes and the length of the edition's existence may reflect more than one copyright date. As long as the editions of the individual components of the math book are the same, the copyright date is not relevant.

Under Saxon Publishers in Norman, Oklahoma, each individual level math book had three components as part of a kit, originally referred to by Saxon Publishers as the Homeschool Kit.

The new Saxon Web site now refers to this as the ***Complete Package,*** and the contents have changed. The specifics of each will be discussed later in the applicable chapter dealing with that specific textbook.

Last, when you buy used Saxon math books, make sure you receive all the support materials with the textbook, and make sure they are all the same edition, because the publisher will not replace any of those component parts for you. In most cases, they are out-of-print, and no longer available from Saxon.

For example, if you find that all three parts of a used second edition of the *Algebra ½* Homeschool Kit are there, go through and make sure all of the pages are there and that all of the tests are in the accompanying ***Test Forms Booklet*** as well.

If they tell you the missing pages or individual tests are available by emailing Saxon – find another merchant!

Student Placement

From my teaching experience, I have learned that the best way to determine where non-Saxon students should start is to have them take the Saxon Middle Grade Placement Test before they proceed into a Saxon math book. The tests are free and are found on the Saxon Homeschool Web site at *www.saxonhomeschool.com.* A direct link to these tests is also provided in my on-line advisory *Homeschool Newsletter* at *www.homeschoolwithsaxon.com.*

These tests can be used in the initial evaluation of non-Saxon students to determine the correct level Saxon math textbook for them. As with every test, it is but one tool in determining where your child should start in the Saxon sequence. The Saxon Middle Grade Placement Test covers material from fourth grade math through pre-algebra (*Math 54* to *Algebra ½*). The upper level placement tests for *Algebra 1* or above can also be found at that same location on the Saxon Homeschool Web site.

Parents should be aware that the tests were designed to place non-Saxon students into the correct level Saxon math book. They were not designed for evaluating students already using a Saxon math book to see what their next Saxon book should be. Using the tests for this purpose will more than likely result in academic problems for students by placing them in the wrong math book.

The tests were not designed to show how intelligent students are, or how much math they know. The tests were designed to uncover what math concepts students have not mastered. A Saxon math student who takes these tests will receive false high test scores.

Over the years, I have also observed that **A Beka Book™** textbooks, through the third or fourth grade, somewhat parallel the methodology of the Saxon textbooks at those same levels. So students who are using them will also receive false high test scores when they take the Saxon Middle Grade Placement Test.

My recommendations to parents whose children are using **A Beka Book™** math books who want to switch to Saxon is to do so in the fourth or fifth grade. Do not have them take the Saxon Middle Grade Placement Test. Move the student from the third or fourth grade level math materials into the appropriate fourth (*Math 54*) or fifth (*Math 65*) grade level Saxon math book.

If the student is already in a Saxon math book at any level, and he satisfactorily completes all the lessons in that math book – and that book was not out-of-date or out-of-print – he should move to the next book in the series.

John Saxon designed his math books as skill level books. Because some homeschool parents do not take summer breaks as the public schools do, it is not uncommon to find a fifth grade homeschool student successfully taking *Math 76* or *Math 87*.

The only criterion to follow is that the student satisfactorily completes all of the problems in all the lessons and takes all of the required tests from the previous Saxon math textbook. The term "satisfactorily completed" means that the student completed all the lessons in the previous book and that he mastered the material with a test average of eighty or better.

The minimal acceptable mastery level on any Saxon test would be a score of eighty. Since there are twenty or more tests to take, a few test scores of seventy or seventy-five are certainly acceptable. This score should be recorded from the first time the student takes the test in a fifty-minute time period. The test answers should be graded as right or wrong – no partial credit!

Why all these restrictions? I recall, many years ago, when I told one parent about the minimum score of eighty, she replied, "Oh, he always gets a ninety or better by the third time he takes the test!"

The most accurate way to evaluate Saxon math students is by looking at the last five or six of the twenty-plus tests they have taken in the book. If these test scores are eighty or above (one or two seventy-fives are all right), then the students have indicated mastery of the material and they are ready for the next book in the series.

Students who move from one math curriculum to another using several math curriculums over several years develop gaps or *holes in mathematic*s in their basic math background. Later, as these students approach the upper level math courses, these deficiencies will present a serious problem for them.

Transferring into Saxon math in *Algebra 1* or *Algebra 2*, or above, requires that the students be well versed in the basics they should have encountered and mastered in the previous textbooks they studied.

The cumulative nature of the John Saxon's math books requires the student to have mastered this previous material. Not having mastered these concepts is what creates problems for students who transfer into the Saxon series. These weaknesses are generally exposed somewhere between lessons thirty and thirty-five in any Saxon math textbook.

Some parents make the mistake of giving their children math books to look at, and to have them flip through the pages to tell them whether or not they know how to do the material. We must be aware of the fact that the teenage brain is not yet mature. The teenager usually will reply, "Sure, I know how to do this stuff."

Now, if adults were replying to that question, they would say, "Yes, I recognize this material because I have encountered it before, but I no longer have any idea of how to do it." The teenager's immature thought process conveniently drops off the part about recognizing, but is no longer able to do it.

If today I were handed a manual on nuclear weapons components, I might look through it and recognize some of the concepts and understand some of the material presented in it, but if you were to ask me any detailed questions about that material, I would be forced to say, "I don't have the foggiest idea."

I have forgotten most, if not all, of that material; and I would need to review it in detail before I answered your question. I don't think you want me firing any rockets or artillery pieces either!

Saxon Placement Tests were designed to highlight those essential math concepts the student has forgotten, or did not master. The tests were not designed to reflect how much the student has learned or how smart the student is. They are only one of several tools that will assist parents in determining if students have retained sufficient basic concepts to enable them to proceed successfully in the next level Saxon math course.

I should discuss one last potential problem area. All of John Saxon's math textbooks contain some level of geometry. Transferring into the Saxon series of math books at the algebra one or algebra two levels without having previously been exposed to any geometry can be frustrating.

The difficulty occurs not just because the student has never been exposed to the basics of geometry, but also because the contents of these two algebra textbooks assume the student has earlier mastered a pre-algebra textbook's content as well. In the Saxon series, *Algebra* ½ is what other publishers refer to as their pre-algebra book.

Using the Books Correctly

The unique *incremental development* process used in John Saxon's math textbooks makes them excellent textbooks for use in either a classroom or homeschool environment. If they are not used correctly in either case, however, they will eventually present a problem for the student.

Some years ago, I was asked to help a school district in the Midwest recover from falling test scores and an increased failure rate in their middle and high school math programs. They had been using, actually misusing, their Saxon math books for several years.

After I had a chance to tell the group of school administrators and teachers some of the reasons for their difficulties, the district superintendent said, "What I hear you saying, Art, is that we bought a new car, and since we already knew how to drive, we saw no reason to read the owner's manual – wouldn't you agree?"

To which I replied, "It's worse than that, sir! You all thought you had purchased a car with an automatic transmission, but Saxon is a stick shift! It is critical that certain procedures be followed, just as well as some be dropped, or you will strip the gears!"

The uniqueness of John Saxon's method of incremental development, coupled with the cumulative nature of the daily work in every Saxon math textbook, requires specific rules be followed to ensure success – and ultimately mastery!

First, the ***ESSENTIAL DO's.***

Do Always Use the Correct Edition. Whether you have a new or used Homeschool Kit or a Complete Package, always make sure it is a valid edition and not an academically weak, older, out-of-print edition.

Do Finish the Book. This is critical to preparing for the next level of material. I once had a superintendent ask me, "Which is more important, mastery or completing the textbook?" To which I replied, "They are synonymous!"

Just as you wouldn't practice only the first half of Beethoven's Fifth Symphony and then go out on the concert tour and play the entire piece – we can easily assume where the mistakes would occur – why wouldn't you study all of the concepts in the entire textbook?

Do All of the Problems - Every Day. There is a reason the problems come in pairs, and it is not so the student can do just the odd or even problems. The two problems are different from each other to keep the student from memorizing the procedure, as opposed to mastering the concept.

Students who cannot complete the thirty problems each day in about an hour are either dawdling, or are at a level of mathematics above their capabilities, based upon their previous math experiences.

Do Follow the Order of the Lessons. Why study both lessons seventeen and eighteen in such and such a book because they both cover the same concept? Why not just skip lesson eighteen and go straight to lesson nineteen?

Why? Because the author took an extremely difficult math concept and separated it into two different lessons. This allowed the student to comprehend the entire concept more easily, a concept which will be presented again in a more challenging way later in lesson twenty-seven of that book!

Do Give All of the Scheduled Tests – On Time. In every test booklet, in front of the printed Test 1 is a schedule for the required tests. ***Not testing*** is not an option!

I have often heard homeschool parents say, "He does so well on his daily work; why test him?" To which I reply, "The results of the daily work reflect memory – the results of the weekly tests reflect mastery!"

Now for the **_ESSENTIAL DON'Ts._**

Don't Skip the First 30 – 35 Lessons in the Book. Many homeschool parents still believe that because the first thirty or so lessons in every Saxon math book appear to be a review of material in the last part of the previous textbook, they can skip them. Let's review the two elements of **_automaticity_** again – **_repetition over time_**!

Yes, some of the early problems in the textbook appear similar to the problems reflected in the last part of the previous textbook. They have, however, been changed from the previous textbook to ensure that the student has mastered the concept.

Remember, the student was supposed to have sixty to ninety days off in the summer. He needs this review! The first lessons in the books thus contain new material as well as some review.

I would add what I have told literally thousands of home school parents these past nine years. "Must students always have to do something they do not know how to do. Why can't they do something they already know how to do?" "What is wrong with building or reinforcing their confidence in mathematics through review?"

Don't Skip Textbooks. Skipping a book in Saxon is like tearing out the middle pages of your piano sheet music and then attempting to play the entire piece while still providing a meaningful musical presentation.

Later in this book, under the specific textbook descriptions, we will discuss any legitimate textbook elimination because of the specific abilities of the individual students.

Don't Skip Problems in the Daily Assignments. When students complain that the daily workload of thirty problems is too much, it is generally the result of one of the following three conditions:

- Students are so involved in a multitude of activities that they cannot spend the hour each day required for Saxon mathematics.

- Students are at a level above their capabilities and unable to adequately process the required concepts in the allotted time because of this difficulty.

- The student is either a dawdler or just lazy!

Doing just the odd or just the even numbered problems in a Saxon math book is not the solution to those difficulties. As I mentioned earlier in the book, there are two of each type of problem for several reasons, and doing just the odd or even is not one of them!

Don't Skip Lessons. Incremental Development literally means introducing complicated math concepts to the students in small increments, rather than having them tackle the entire concept at once. It is essential that students do a lesson a day and take a test every four to five lessons, depending on what book they are using. So what happens when you skip an easy lesson or two?

Very simply, the student cannot process the new material satisfactorily without having had a chance to read about it, and to understand its characteristics. Some students attempt to fix this shortcoming by then working on several lessons in a single day, to catch up to where they should be in the book. This technique is also not recommended. As John Saxon would tell you, "The only way to eat an elephant is one bite at a time."

Here is a general overview of what the parent/teacher and the student would encounter in a typical math day.

At the start of the school day, the parent collects the completed previous daily assignment from the student. Students should have access to the answers in the answer booklet after doing their daily work to check questionable answers before they turn in the completed assignment.

They should not have access to the **solutions manual**, as that does not stimulate mastery. Upon receiving the completed assignment, the parent then asks the student whether or not he has read the lesson for today.

While John Saxon's math books were originally written as skill level books to be taken sequentially, the books have been written at the appropriate grade reading level. Students can easily read the textbooks on their own.

It should be the student's responsibility to spend fifteen to twenty minutes each day in reading the daily lesson and then asking the parent questions as necessary. Some parents may want to become more directly involved in the teaching process. There is nothing wrong with the parent actually teaching the lesson to the student if necessary.

Upon completion of the reading of the new lesson by the student, the parent should then ask the student if he understands the new concept. If the student says he has read and understands the new concept, then the parent should ask the student to orally explain it.

If the student says he cannot explain it, or if he doesn't explain it very well, the parent should ask the student to do one or two of the practice problems from that lesson.

This is done to determine if the student has, in fact, learned the new lesson, but is just having trouble explaining it. Or, perhaps the student does not understand the concept and needs additional help. If necessary, the parent then goes over the lesson with the student at this time to assist in the learning process.

While there may be as many as five or more practice problems, the parent needs use only as many as necessary with the student to enable him to indicate that he has acquired a basic understanding of the new concept.

Some lessons discuss more than one concept. This occurs when the concepts are considered fairly simple by the author and not considered to be challenging to the average student. If the student does experience trouble with multiple concepts, the parent may go back and review the material from that lesson again the next day to reinforce the material.

Another solution would be to take two days for a particularly difficult lesson. The parent could go over one of the concepts the first day and the student does just the odd numbered problems. Then on the second day, the parent could go over the second concept and the student does just the even numbered problems. This way, the student does all of the problems in the lesson; it just takes two days to complete them, as opposed to one, because of the difficulty with the concept(s) of the lesson.

Remember, not all students will completely understand the concept in their first encounter with it. It may take several days, and the parent may have to watch the daily assignments for the next few days to see if the student is finally grasping the new concept.

Upon passing that hurdle, the student then sets out to complete the assigned thirty or so problems. Meanwhile the parent takes a few minutes to review the daily assignment the student just handed in for completeness and to notice any glaring shortcomings.

28

How important is it for the students to do their daily practice problems?

I told my students that if they did not want to practice "putting" on a daily basis, they should forget placing in any golf tournament. If they were tired of the daily "batting practice," they should not complain about a low batting average.

For more than a decade while teaching with John Saxon's math books, I have probably heard every excuse by students as to why they were either beginning to fail, or were already failing their math course!

To make it easier for them, I compiled a list of excuses they could use. This way, when asked by their parents why they were failing, they could just give them a number, rather than a long excuse for their predicament.

I thought it might help to copy them here, in case they are needed in your homeschool classroom. The three easiest ways to fail a Saxon math course are:

1.   DON'T DO THE DAILY ASSIGNMENTS. "Why should I be required to do all this boring *make-work* stuff when I already know it? I read the lesson every day and I understand what the lesson is all about. Why should I have to waste my time doing all of these problems just to keep me busy? I know this stuff! Besides, I have a job after school and I don't have the time. "

2.   COPY SOMEONE ELSE'S WORK. "My friend writes neater than I do and besides, I know how to do this 'dumb stuff.' I just don't have the time and you won't accept reproduced copies, so my friend copies it for me. Sometimes I copy it myself and it is just like doing it myself because I learn as I write it down."

3. WRITE DOWN JUST THE ANSWERS. "Most of the time I use 'scratch paper' to show my work, but it is too messy to turn in, so I just neatly write down the answer so you know I did the problem correctly. Besides, I can do this 'stuff' in my head. All you need is just the answer so you know I can do the work."

Remember, the student does not have to invent a new and lengthy reason for his difficulty. He just needs to tell you if he is applying standard excuse one, two or three!

There is not much to reviewing the homework, except to see that they have the correct answers and to look for any unanswered problems or unexplained answers. That is, did the student do all of the problems correctly and did he show his work? [If the calculations are simple enough to be worked in the student's head, they need not be shown.]

If the student left some problems blank, did he do that several days in a row? Were they always the same concept? Leaving blanks may indicate that the student does not know how to work a particular concept and that immediate help is needed.

There is a box at the top of each lesson in *Math 54* through *Math 87*. This box contains *Facts Practice* guidance, *Mental Math* problems and a *Problem Solving* challenge. The exercises offer an opportunity for parents to take a few minutes with their child and see how their skills in these areas are developing.

By the time most students satisfactorily complete *Math 76*, the Facts Practice skills should already be mastered. For a very few students, these drills may then be discontinued in *Math 87* if no longer needed on a daily basis. Instructions for the *Facts Practice* drills are printed in the preface of each Saxon math book.

There is no lesson assignment on test days!

Grading Tests and Daily Assignments

One of the problems homeschool parents encounter when their children use John Saxon's math books is the inclination to academically beat up on them. Now I am not implying physical abuse. But to the students, it does appear to be some form of mental abuse when they have to keep doing their daily work over and over and over again, until they have it one hundred percent correct!

Students seem to put on a different hat, so to speak, when taking a test. Some students permit minor mistakes in their daily work, rather than wasting valuable time correcting them. They appear to take on a different thought process (wear a different hat) when taking a test. They enter a sort of test mode, if you will.

Remember our discussion about the corporate approach of managing by exception? What makes using that technique so applicable to the Saxon math environment is that there is a scheduled test to be taken every four or five lessons, depending on the level of the book being used. This ensures that the parent is only four to five days away from finding out the student's shortcomings and stepping in to correct them in a timely manner.

In *Math 54* through *Math 87*, tests are taken every five lessons. Beginning with *Algebra ½* and through *Calculus* and *Physics*, tests will be taken after every four lessons. Students will then take a weekly test beginning with *Algebra ½*.

Establishing the student's overall grade average [using weekly test scores as well as grades for the daily work] is only one part of the challenge facing homeschool parents. They must also provide an accurate assessment for the tests, and that requires grading them.

There are twenty questions on every math test from *Math 54* through *Advanced Mathematics*. Each individual question, then, is worth five points.

A student can receive four wrong answers on each test and still maintain a minimal mastery level of eighty percent, a solid B, without receiving any partial credit.

It may seem a bit harsh not to permit partial credit, but partial credit is like a federal or state social program. Its application is well intended but never really applied evenly across the spectrum.
Giving partial credit is subjective. Who is to say the mother's partial credit on a particular problem is any fairer than the father's partial credit would be?

I would ask the parents to tell their homeschool students what I as a mathematician and an engineer told my classroom students, "There is no partial credit in real life, so why start here? If you work for a construction company on a highway construction project and you design seven of the nine pre-stressed steel girders correctly on a bridge being constructed, how much partial credit do you get when that bridge comes down? "

After being denied partial credit for leaving off the units (e.g., writing 12 rather than 12 cm), the student will most likely reply, "But, Mom, I got the problem correct. All I left off were the units, and their not that important." To which I reply to the parents, "The next time he asks for twelve dollars, give him a dime and two pennies and remind him that he said the units were not important!"

Using these examples, you will have the teenager's attention and save hours of arguing about partial credit! Then the question arises, "Why is each problem worth five points? Shouldn't each test question be weighted according to its difficulty?"

What may be difficult for one student may be easy for another, so attempting to weight individual problems using different values is less fair than leaving them all of equal value.

Another question frequently asked is, "When some problems have two parts and the students do one part right, why not give them partial credit for the part they have correct?" If there are multiple parts to a test question, they are generally related in either required data or concept; and if one part is wrong, the student evidently did not understand the entire question, and therefore the entire question is wrong.

Still another question that homeschool parents frequently ask is, "What grading scale should I use?" While it would be most admirable to use the old grading scales of 95 – 100 for an A, and 89 – 94 for a B, etc., the rest of the world your child is competing against for scholarships is using a 90, 80, 70, and 60 grading scale.

I would recommend that you do the same. Receiving a solid C from test scores graded strictly on a right or wrong basis in any of John Saxon's math books is equal to a B in any other math textbook or grading system in the public school system.

The last area of grading to discuss is, "How should we weight the daily work and tests?" Because the test grades reflect mastery of the subject material, test grades should comprise 80% – 90% of the student's grade. The daily assigned work then should comprise no more than the remaining 20% - 10% of the grade.

John Saxon's math books were designed to be cumulative in nature. Students who cannot get above a sixty or sixty-five on their tests still are learning! Remember, the material is becoming increasingly more difficult. They just cannot grasp all of the new material as it is presented. Something is keeping them from sufficiently absorbing these new concepts.

These consistently low test scores generally are a sign that that the student is "drowning," and needs immediate help before he can successfully move on to the next book in the Saxon series. They are usually the result of either skipping lessons, skipping an entire book, or of not finishing the previous Saxon math book.

There are twenty or more tests in every one of John Saxon's math books. Since the contents of each test are cumulative, students should be rewarded for what they have learned, not punished for what they did not learn.

I highly recommend the lowest five or six test scores for each course be dropped (unless they are the last five or six in the book) before averaging the students' test grades for the year.

Tests for *Calculus* are set up a bit differently because of the difficulty of the material presented in that textbook. *Calculus* tests do not have twenty questions. The tests may vary from between thirteen and seventeen questions, depending on the material covered in the test, and they need to be graded differently.

You might have noticed that the public and private school teachers have both an A and a B version of the test forms while homeschool parents have only a single version of the tests.

The classroom teacher has the second version to use as a make-up test for students who missed the regular test to prevent them from getting a "heads up" on the answers from their friends. A second version of the tests is not necessary for homeschool use.

The homeschool tests contain the same concepts and degree of difficulty as the classroom test masters do, but the individual questions are different from the classroom versions, for obvious reasons.

Use of Calculators

Ask eighth or ninth grade students what the square root of 169, 196, or 225 is and you will be listening to a very long silence coupled with receiving an equally long blank stare from them. Then ask them what the product of 5280 x 5280 would be.

Following their frantic search for the calculator you have hidden, you will find that without the calculator, most young students cannot even estimate the answer for you. The answer will be a bit larger than 25,000,000, but an estimate of 5 x 5 plus six zeros, would be a pretty close answer.

This concept of using scientific notation to estimate the multiplication of large numbers was introduced in both *Math 87* and *Algebra ½.*

Checking our answer with a calculator, we would find the product of 5280 x 5280 to actually be 27,878,400. But what if students just blindly punched in the numbers, and left off a zero? How would they know that 2,787,840 is not the correct answer to the product of 5280 x 5280?

When I approach parents and teachers with these questions, a student will invariably say to me, "But you're smarter than I am." To which I reply, "I am not smarter than you, I am just older than you. And it is not that I do not like calculators; I do use one, but only when absolutely necessary."

Have them add the numbers 2386 + 3588 + 2986 and tell them, before they actually add them, to first "estimate" what the answer will be. Then have them add the numbers on paper and see if they added them correctly. Whether or not they use a calculator, their answer has to be a shade smaller than the sum of 24 + 36 + 30 + two more zeroes, or slightly smaller than 9000!

I will wager the average eighth or ninth grade math student cannot estimate the process of either adding or multiplying large numbers. This is why John Saxon did not believe in the student using a calculator until the last twenty or so lessons in algebra one. And I agree with him! There are not too many problems in the last few lessons of *Algebra 1* that allows use of the calculator anyway.

Actually, the scientific calculator is not really needed until lesson forty-three of *Algebra 2,* when trigonometric functions are first introduced. Letting students become familiar with a calculator late in *Algebra 1*, however, makes using one easier when they get to *Algebra 2.*

There is a certain satisfaction in being able to estimate the result of multiplying 5,500,310 times 2,206,213 without a calculator, and then, taking pencil and paper, seeing how close you came. I would estimate, as the *Algebra ½* student should also, that the answer will be slightly larger than (6 x 2) followed by twelve zeroes.

Another problem that arises for students using a scientific calculator too early in mathematics is the damage done as they learn where and how to use the fraction key on the calculator before they know how to find common denominators correctly!

There is a *fraction key* found on modern scientific calculators. This key enables students using one of them to add two fractions with different denominators without first having to find their common denominator. The calculator does it for them!

Now what do those young students do when, later in an algebra one course, they encounter the addition of two algebraic fractions?
When they encounter a/b + c/d, not having learned how to calculate common denominators with numbered fractions, they will not have the faintest idea of how to acquire a common denominator using lettered variables.

I am sadly reminded of the fourth grade math teacher who, when asked about the difficulty in teaching fractions to fourth graders, wailed at me, "I have neither the time nor the patience to teach them fractions. I give them a calculator and show them how to use the fraction key." Years later, I had some of her students in my *Algebra 1* class. They were failing because they could not decipher simple algebraic functions which required using common denominators.

A good quarterback needs to be able to think fast and make correct decisions in fractions of a second. Mental manipulation of numbers or use of pen and paper to quickly multiply or divide trains the mind to do what good quarterbacking requires. We cripple our students when allowing them to use calculators at young ages and deny them the confidence that comes with fast, accurate thinking.

Like the slide rules we carried to engineering classes more than fifty years ago, the calculator is but a tool to help the student speed up the tedious process of data manipulation to determine the correct answer. The student should command the calculator, not the other way around.

I recently read an article that said a university had found that the old slide rule we used was not as slow as originally thought. They had tested the slide rule against a computer calculating the same data, and they found an engineer using the slide rule was capable of calculating some engineering formulas faster than the computer.

An interesting observation I made was that most math teachers today no longer remember or teach what engineering notation is. We teach students only about scientific notation. We no longer teach them about engineering notation because we no longer use slide rules, for which the use of engineering notation was essential.

When the time is right for the student to use a calculator, make sure it is a scientific calculator and not an adding machine. Regardless of how old the scientific calculator is, if it still works, use it!

Scientific calculators will have keys labeled **log, ln, cos, sin, and tan,** on them. You can check to see if it is a scientific calculator by entering **2 + 4 x 3.** If the answer you receive is **14**, it is a scientific calculator.

If the answer you receive is **18**, it is not a scientific calculator. It does not contain the microchip that applies the order of operations used in mathematics.

Oh, yes, I almost forgot. The square roots of 169, 196, and 225 are 13, 14 and 15 respectively!

Graphing vs. Scientific Calculators

The first calculator I ever laid eyes on was a large handheld gadget about three-quarters the size of a small pocket novel. It had a red display, or readout, and it was a lot thicker than this book.

It was absolutely useless to me, being colorblind. Later, when the manufacturers switched to a green or gray readout, I could finally discern the data.

If I recall correctly, this particular calculator initially cost more than fifty dollars. As a financially strapped college student attending college on the GI Bill, I did not want to spend all that money. After all, I still had my trusty slide rule and book of logarithmic and trigonometric functions. What else did I need?

Today, the parent is faced with the dilemma of spending ten to fifteen dollars for a scientific calculator or about one hundred ten dollars for a graphing calculator.

I can assure you, the graphing calculator will not increase the student's knowledge of algebraic, geometric, logarithmic or trigonometric functions, or their ability to do them, so why buy one?

The graphing calculators sold today are powerful instructional aids; calculations for algebra, geometry, trigonometry, and calculus however, can still all be done easily and accurately with the old, inexpensive scientific calculator.

No math textbook that I am currently aware of teaches the student both how to do the math and also how to use the graphing calculator – or any calculator for that matter! And it is not by accident that the booklet accompanying the graphing calculator is over a half inch thick!

What never ceases to amaze me is when students complain about how difficult it is to find the necessary key strokes for the math functions on their graphing calculator. Yet they never fail to learn which keys to use to play the games on them.

As any mathematician would tell the reader, the graphing calculator has certainly improved to become a powerful tool in the hands of the mathematician. Like the slide-rule of fifty years ago, however, the graphing calculator is not a substitute for the knowledge and ability of the individual student.

The graphing calculator will not solve the problem by itself. Students still need to be able to understand and solve the problem before they use new technology to speed up that process.

There are some educators who will tell you that students taking the ACT or SAT exams are at a disadvantage using a scientific rather than a graphing calculator. I will tell you that students using a scientific calculator – that they have mastered – are better off than the students who use a graphing calculator they are not familiar with.

They end up wasting their valuable time and energy trying to use a powerful piece of technology they have not yet mastered. And their math scores suffer!

If you feel your son or daughter needs a graphing calculator, that is fine. There is absolutely nothing wrong with using one. Make sure, however, that you enroll them in a summer school or evening course at the local university or technical school in a course titled *How to Use a Graphing Calculator.*

Learning beforehand how to properly use the graphing calculator will enable them to spend their time working and understanding the math functions, rather than trying to figure out what keys on their expensive calculator they should use.

There are a number of excellent graphing calculators on the market today. Their prices range from eighty to one hundred twenty dollars. Any one of them will satisfy the student's needs. I am, however, more familiar with **Casio®** and **Texas Instruments®** brands. Both have tutorial Web sites for users of their graphing calculators.

Their tutorial Web sites present easily followed examples to walk the student through particularly difficult operations not easily understood from the written instructions. Both companies also offer toll free technical assistance as well.

These Web site links as well as the toll free telephone numbers for both companies are posted in my on-line advisory *Homeschool Newsletter* at *www.homeschoolwithsaxon.com.*

Using Supplemental or Tutorial Instructional Materials

Whenever I encountered students who were finding themselves in academic trouble, I would check to see what their math background was.

For example, students who were not doing well early in *Algebra 1* usually either just finished *Algebra ½* with a D, or had not completed the entire book.

In any math textbook, if the student starts getting into academic trouble, the parents generally seek help. They either hire a tutor or buy some tutorial or supplemental program.

There are a myriad of homeschool distributors who profess to provide good supplemental programs for John Saxon's math books. Still other programs profess to provide special tutoring for the Saxon math student to help them do better.

These programs are most often sold as CD's, DVD's, or video cassettes. Because the student's problem is the result of an inadequate math background, these solutions will not usually help.

It's like standing on a bridge watching someone drown in the water below. You can jump in and pull that person safely to shore, but that is certainly not the time or the place to try to teach him how to swim!

Just as it is not possible to teach a drowning person how to swim while he is drowning, it also is not possible to teach a math student new math concepts while he is failing! Mathematics is cumulative, and one cannot learn new concepts while failing the old ones.

John Saxon did not produce, distribute, or endorse any of these supplemental or tutorial programs, and I would not endorse them either because they do not adequately teach or tutor. Students, who cannot understand the material they are failing, are more than likely using a book above their capabilities.

Most of the programs I have reviewed that purport to be tutorial packages for John Saxon's math books do little more than read the book to the student and go over the examples already printed in the textbook.

I do not understand why anyone would spend hundreds of dollars to have someone read the book to their child, especially when that person is neither a qualified mathematician nor an experienced Saxon math teacher!

If parents want to buy the product to use for their own review before they teach the lesson to the student that would certainly be helpful to them. Or if the student has a reading disorder and the oral presentation will help, that is also a great idea.

John Saxon's math books, however, are easy to read. They have been evaluated as being written at a reading level equal to or below the grade level of the book. *Algebra ½, Algebra 1,* and *Algebra 2* all are written at the eighth grade reading level. *Calculus* is written at a tenth grade reading level.

So many times I have heard homeschool parents say to me that they believed using the CD, DVD, or video cassette helped their son or daughter because they did not like to read the book.

The alarming fact is that to be successful in upper level mathematics and science, students must have already developed the habit of reading and researching. They will not find these concepts on their TV screen in some action movie or in an on-line computer program.

The products on the market today that I have reviewed will not solve the problem for a failing child when that failure stems from previous materials they have not mastered.

More than likely these students fall into one or more of the following groups. They:

- Skipped the previous Saxon math textbook.

- Did not finish the previous Saxon math textbook.

- Did only the odd or even numbered problems and therefore did not fully master the concepts in the previous book.

- Never took any tests in the previous book and therefore we cannot judge what they did or did not master in the previous materials.

- Grouped lessons together and did only partial homework assignments so they could finish the textbook in less than one hundred and twenty days.

- Came from a lower-level non-Saxon math book, and are therefore unable to understand the concepts of the Saxon book they are now using.

- Were never tested to see what textbook in John Saxon's math series they should have started with.

There are several others, but you get the idea. There are no easy or simple solutions to correcting student failure.

44

Helping Struggling Students

Each chapter in this book dealing with the individual level textbooks contains information about the prerequisites for that specific course. Regardless of how well students may have done in their previous math books, however, they can still encounter difficulty in their current textbooks.

Before we discuss these individual situations, parents should first evaluate the students' test grades; for example, are they rising, falling or holding steady? Do the last five or so test scores reflect scores of 55, 65, 70, 70, 75 etc., or 90, 80, 70, 70, 65, etc?

The former group of scores reflects students who are learning and absorbing the new material, having first encountered concepts they were not familiar with. The latter group reflects students who have encountered material for which they have not been properly prepared.

Parents have told me, "But he does so well on his daily work, and now he has started doing poorly on his tests. I don't understand why." My answer to that is that the student is probably doing what I refer to as "back-pedaling."

What that means is the student has access to the answers while doing his daily work. So when he encounters a problem he cannot set up or solve, he looks at the answer and from it figures out how to set up and solve the problem. The student cannot do this "back-pedaling" on the test, however, because he has no answer to look up.

He cannot set up or solve the test question because there is no answer to use as a guide. In other words, the student has no idea of what to do. He has not mastered the concept. He has just memorized a routine that requires having the answer to work backwards from when solving the problem.

For that reason students should not be allowed to refer to the answer booklet until after they have completed their assignments and have a need to check their work.

Daily work should be considered as practice and not weighted heavily. Parents should rely upon test scores to indicate mastery of the material. Remember, the cumulative nature of John Saxon's math books allows students to have lower test scores in the beginning of a textbook. So long as their later test scores increase above seventy-five, they will have indicated mastery of the material necessary for success in the next book.

As we said earlier, we want to reward students for their successes and not punish them for earlier failures. With twenty or more tests in every math course from *Math 54* to *Calculus*, students can easily drop five to six low test scores from earlier in the course and have their test averages still indicate mastery of the material for success in the next course.

I believe it is important to discuss various ways parents can assist students who encounter difficulty even after allegedly mastering the recommended prerequisites for the course. Students who encounter difficulties in one of John Saxon's math books generally fall into one of four categories.

1. They encounter difficulty before reaching lesson thirty.

2. They have passed lesson thirty, are somewhere in the middle of the book, and are now encountering difficulty as exhibited by test scores below seventy.

3. They are near the end of the book and their test scores are starting to fall below seventy.

4. They are students with special learning requirements who may encounter difficulty anywhere in the book.

Let's discuss what to do with students in the **first category,** those who start out with low test scores even before they reach lesson thirty or so in the book. Earlier, I used the phrase after *allegedly mastering the prerequisites.* I used that phrase because, while students may have received passing grades, they did not master the material.

The parent might have awarded excessive partial credit on the tests for any number of reasons. They might have allowed the student to do only the odd numbered problems, allowed the student to skip what they considered an easy lesson, or any number of other short-cuts.

Perhaps the student was even allowed to use the solutions manual as a guide in doing his daily work. Allowing students to use the solutions manual this way gives them an opportunity to get their daily assignment done and not have to master the concepts because they have the solutions manual to guide them.

Rather than mastering the individual concepts, students learn to memorize the steps and know ahead of time that if they cannot do the problem, they can always trace the steps in the solutions manual. Add to this problem the fact that the parents may be using homework to determine the student's grades and not the required tests, and you have a perfect formula for disaster, because the students are not mastering the material. They are memorizing it!

Because John Saxon's math books require mastery and not memory, there is not much a parent can do if the student is struggling in the early part of the textbook.

Without exception, every parent I have talked with over the past eight years whose child was in this situation admitted to allowing the student to use some form or other of deviation or shortcut in the previous textbooks.

If children are failing or experiencing test scores below seventy in their current textbook, and they have not yet gone beyond lesson thirty or so, please read the individual chapter for their specific textbook for advice on how to correct this problem.

If the child has special learning requirements, skip to the last part of this chapter (the fourth and final category on page 51).

The **second category** of students are those who are somewhere in the middle of the book. Their problem is a bit more difficult to quantify because the reasons are not as obvious as those revealed by students experiencing difficulties in the early part of the book.

Remember those "holes in mathematics" we discussed earlier? Even though the students have successfully and correctly completed the previous Saxon math book, they may still have difficulty with specific math concepts.

These "holes" are now becoming more and more obvious as concepts are being combined. Individual concepts become more and more dependent upon earlier learned concepts which may not yet have been mastered. For example, students who have mastered concepts A, B and C but did not master concept D are not aware of the pending problem, and may not consider concept D very critical.

Perhaps this concept was introduced late in the previous text or earlier in the student's current book. Later on in his current book, however, combining concepts A and B is not a problem, but when concepts C and D are combined the student is unable to master this new concept.

Reviewing the tests allows the parents to focus on these problem areas and gives them time to provide additional review or assistance when necessary. You can always have these students go back ten or more lessons and start over.

This review process will not work if the students are in a book above their capabilities, but if they just need a review because they dropped a little behind in their work or did not quite understand a concept or two in the previous week or so, it will enable them to catch up.

Another technique to use is to take more than one day for an extremely difficult concept, or when more than one concept is presented in a single lesson. While the author might have thought the combined concepts were rather easy, the student may be experiencing difficulty with them for any number of reasons.

When this technique is used, assign the odd problems the first day and the even problems the second day. This way the students encounter all required concepts both days. <u>Do not</u>, for instance, let them do problems 1-15 one day and then problems 16-30 the second day.

Remember, public and private schools have 175 - 180 school days, but they lose about thirty of them because of any number of mandatory assemblies, sporting events, etc. Homeschool parents have these thirty extra days to use for such a review process when necessary.

This stepping back and reviewing technique may be necessary more than once, but it is essential for success by weaker math students who encounter difficulties with some math concepts that others do not.

The **third category** is the most difficult to correct. These are the students who are near the end of the book and their test scores are dropping.

The problems encountered by these students may be the result of any number of situations, including boredom with studying, family problems created by moving, or other personal relationships.

I recall a young straight - A student in one of my *Algebra 1* classes who witnessed his young Labrador retriever puppy being run over by a truck. He was not the same student as before the accident. He eventually had to repeat the course. I attributed his eventual A in the course the second year to the fact that his grandparents gave him a Labrador puppy that summer.

The last third of the lessons in Saxon math books take concepts already learned, combine them, and then present them in a more challenging manner.

New concepts necessary for success in the next level textbook are also introduced. While some of these same concepts will be re-introduced in the early lessons of the next level math book, they are first introduced here at a more understandable level of difficulty.

The early contents of the next textbook will assume that students have already been exposed to these concepts in a simpler form. Because it is this last third of the Saxon math books that prepares students for the rigors of the next level math book, test grades in these last five or so tests, then, are what provide an indication as to how successful these students will be in that next level textbook.

As we said earlier, minimal mastery is reflected by a test score of at least an eighty. Certainly one or two test grades of seventy-five among these last five or so tests are not that damaging, especially considering there is no partial credit being given.

Five or six test scores of seventy or seventy-five, while certainly acceptable, give an indication, however, that the student will eventually encounter difficulty in the next level book. Parents need to correct the problem before moving to the next book. The review process discussed above is one way to allow the student sufficient time to recover.

50

Another procedure that will reveal where the problems started is to retest the students in an earlier test. Go back about five tests from where the students are now and have them take that test to see if there are some specific concepts they may be having problems with.

The results of this test will reveal where the students still have some weaknesses. Certainly, if the students score less than an eighty, there are some concepts they have not yet mastered.

If this occurs, switch to two days per lesson for the last twenty or so lessons in the book. Use the extra time each day for the students to go back and review those earlier concepts they are still having trouble with.

The **fourth and final category** deals with students who have special needs. This category presents a myriad of questions that cannot all be answered to everyone's satisfaction, but there are several ways to help students who are educationally challenged.

The incremental development of Saxon math textbooks lends itself to use by students with special learning requirements because they can break the lessons into even smaller increments to suit their needs.

Consider any or all of the following suggestions to help students with special learning requirements:

- Take two days for each lesson, doing odd numbered problems the first day and even numbered problems the second day. If necessary, take three days, and do just ten problems each day. This extends the students' school year to a full twelve months, but if that is what needs to be done, it is not impossible.

- Purchase a CD, DVD or video program designed to supplement Saxon math books and allow the students an opportunity to listen to the lesson either before or after reading the lesson in the book.

- Reproduce the pages of the book using larger sized font for students with the need for larger print. Do the same for the tests.

- Give the test in two increments of ten questions each with an hour in between each test segment.

Students placed in my classroom that had special learning requirements did far better on state mandated tests than those placed in a special education lab. Homeschool parents will find that using John Saxon's math textbooks will greatly enhance their ability to help their children successfully advance.

There are special adaptations for some of the middle grade math textbooks, and parents should contact the **Saxon®** customer service desk at 1-800-284-7019 between the hours of 8:30 a.m. and 4:30 p.m. (CST) to check for their availability. The newer editions did not, however, have them at the time of this publishing. You can also check the on-line advisory *Homeschool Newsletter* at *www. homeschoolwithsaxon.com* for updated information.

Math 54

NOTE: Before reading this chapter, make sure you have read the foreword.

Math 54 normally is used as a fourth grade math textbook, the first hardcover textbook students encounter in John Saxon's math series. The text immediately follows *Math 3,* or whatever third grade math book or math series the student just completed.

In a few states, like California, *Math 54* is required to be used in the third grade. If the family is currently living in California, I recommend the parents first check with the California Board of Education before using *Math 54* as a fourth grade textbook.

The Saxon Middle Grade Placement Test score or some other testing criterion may reflect the student's ability to skip *Math 54* and move immediately to *Math 65*; I would not, however, recommend skipping *Math 54* on the basis of either one of those tests alone.

Before considering skipping *Math 54* and moving the student directly into *Math 65*, do this simple evaluation. Give the child Test 21 from the old hardcover second edition or Test 19 from the new softcover third edition of *Math 54*.

Give the student no more than forty-five minutes without a calculator and grade each problem as right or wrong. No partial credit! If that test score is eighty-five or better, the student can then safely move to either the second or third edition of *Math 65.*

In all the years that I have advised both homeschool parents and classroom teachers, there have been fewer than a handful of students who have successfully gone from a third grade math book straight to *Math 65.* Every one of them received a score of eighty-five or better on that test under the above criteria.

There are only two editions of *Math 54* that homeschool parents should consider using. They are the older hardcover second edition and the new softcover third edition. While the hardcover second edition textbook has been out of print for several years, it is still an excellent textbook to use in preparing students for *Math 65* that follows.

Both the older hardcover second editions and the new softcover third editions have lesson reference numbers, as well as step-by-step solutions to the tests. While support materials from the new third edition are not compatible with the older second edition textbook, the difficulty and mathematical content of both editions remain almost identical.

Their specific differences are itemized below.

1. Twelve lessons from the old second edition were converted to *Investigations* in the new third edition.

2. Four lessons from the old second edition were re-titled as *Additional Topics* at the end of the new third edition textbook.

3. Several less challenging concepts were consolidated into individual lessons, giving the new third edition a total of one hundred thirty-six lessons as opposed to the old second edition, which has one hundred forty-one.

4. The total numbers of tests was reduced from twenty-eight in the old second edition to twenty-three in the new third edition.

5. A step-by-step solutions manual was added.

The older second edition of *Math 54* has three components which were referred to by Saxon Publishers as the *Homeschool Kit.*

These components include:

- A hardcover student textbook.

- A softcover Home Study Packet that contains the test solutions, answers to all the problems in the daily assignments, and answers to the Facts Practice Tests.

- A softcover Test Forms Booklet that contains the twenty-eight tests and the Facts Practice Test Forms.

If parents want to buy a used copy of the *Math 54* second edition, they should check to make sure that:

- All three components are there.

- All three have SECOND EDITION printed on the front covers.

- All of the pages and tests are inside the two booklets, as well as the testing schedule. The test schedule is printed opposite Test 1.

Using soft covers for the new third edition of *Math 54* originated with Saxon Publishers in Norman, Oklahoma. The company wanted to add a solutions manual to the new editions of the *Math 54* through *Math 87* Homeschool Kit without increasing the overall cost, so they used a softcover for the student textbook.

This new third edition of *Math 54* also has three components. What Saxon Publishers previously referred to as the *Homeschool Kit* is now referred to as the *Complete Package.*

I never found out why the new owners of Saxon changed the title. I suspect it was a decision made by the new marketing staff.

The three components of the new third edition of the *Math 54 Complete Package* include:

- A softcover student textbook.

- A solutions manual that contains step-by-step solutions to the practice and mixed practice problems from the Daily Lessons, Investigations, Appendix Topics, the Supplemental Practice, the Facts Practice Tests, and the Tests.

- A Tests and Worksheets Booklet that contains the Facts Practice Tests, the Activity Sheets, twenty-three tests, and the optional Recording Forms which can be photo-copied.

The solutions manual and the other support materials that come with the new third edition of *Math 54* are not compatible with the older second edition.

These new third editions have been in print for a number of years and are also now available in the used book marketplace. If parents buy one they should make sure all three components are there and that all of the pages and tests are there as well.

Some parents may want the student to skip the first twenty or so lessons in the book because they appear to be almost like the last part of the *Math 3* course. Or, they may allow the student to skip the last twenty or so lessons, because they believe that material will be repeated in the early part of *Math 65*. Either of these shortcuts is likely to harm the student's ability to master the essential math concepts.

Remember, it is confidence building for students to be able to review and do math concepts they are already familiar with. That is part of the process that develops mastery.

As I commented earlier in the book, parents should not fall victim to the old rumor that these sections are only review and that the student can move more quickly through the series if he skips one or both of these sections. What is the rush?

If students are prepared for an algebra one course by the eighth grade, they will be in a calculus textbook their senior year, and prepared for math at any university.

It is critical to make sure the students are well-grounded in the basics of mathematics and that they have no conceptual weaknesses which have developed because they skipped over material.

Mathematics is like swimming – or drowning! It is far easier to teach children how to swim in shallow water than to wait until they get into the deep water – over their heads. It is not possible to teach drowning children how to swim - while they are drowning!

Math 65

NOTE: Before reading this chapter, make sure you have read the foreword.

Math 65 is a fifth grade math textbook. It should be used following successful completion of *Math 54*. If the students used *Math 54,* do not use the Saxon Middle Grade Placement Test to evaluate their progress in this book because they will receive false high test scores. Please read the earlier chapter on *Student Placement.*

Students who have just completed some other fourth grade series math program should also be placed in *Math 65*. Do not skip *Math 65* just because the early few lessons in the textbook appear to repeat what the student may have already studied.

If parents are not sure whether or not the students' previous non-Saxon course was a fourth or fifth grade course and they are considering skipping *Math 65* and starting them with *Math 76*, they should perform this simple evaluation first.

Give the students Test 22 from the older hardcover second edition or Test 20 from the new softcover third edition of *Math 65.* Give them no more than forty-five minutes without a calculator and grade each problem as right or wrong. No partial credit!

If students receive a test score of eighty-five or better on that test, they can then safely move to either the older hardcover third edition or the new softcover fourth edition of *Math 76.*

As with *Math 54* discussed earlier, there are only two editions of *Math 65* that homeschool parents should consider using for fifth grade students. They are the older hardcover second edition and the new softcover third edition.

Even though the older hardcover second edition textbook of *Math 65* has been out of print for several years, it is still an excellent textbook to use in preparing students for *Math 76*.

Both the old hardcover second edition and new softcover third editions of *Math 65* have lesson reference numbers, as well as step-by-step solutions to the tests. While support materials from the new third edition are not compatible with the older second edition textbooks, the difficulty and mathematical content of both editions remain almost identical.

Specific differences between the two editions are itemized below.

1. Eleven of the lessons from the older second edition were converted to *Investigations* in the new third edition. A twelfth investigation dealing with tessellations was added at the end of the new edition.

2. Three *Additional Topics* were added at the end of the new third edition textbook. Two of them introduce Roman Numerals. The third topic introduces the concept of the base 5 number system.

3. Several less challenging concepts were consolidated into individual lessons, giving the new third edition a total of one hundred thirty-five lessons as opposed to the older second edition, which has one hundred forty.

4. The number of tests was reduced from twenty-eight in the older second edition to twenty-three in the new third edition.

5. A step-by-step solutions manual was added.

The three components of the older second edition of *Math 65* were originally referred to by Saxon Publishers as the *Homeschool Kit*.

The three components include:

- A hardcover student textbook.

- A softcover Home Study Packet that contains test solutions, answers to all the problems in the daily assignments, and answers to the Facts Practice Tests.

- A softcover Test Forms Booklet that contains the twenty-eight tests and the Facts Practice Test Forms.

If parents want to buy a used copy of the older second edition of *Math 65,* they should check to make sure that:

- All three components are there.

- All three have SECOND EDITION printed on the front covers.

- All of the pages and tests are inside the two booklets, as well as the testing schedule which is printed opposite Test 1.

Using soft covers for the new third edition of *Math 65* originated with the Saxon Publishers in Norman, Oklahoma. The company wanted to add a solutions manual to the new editions of the *Math 54* through *Math 87* Homeschool Kit without increasing the overall cost, so they used soft covers for the student textbook.

The new third edition of *Math 65* also has three components. But what Saxon Publishers previously called the *Homeschool Kit* is now referred to as the *Complete Package.* I never found out why the new owners of Saxon changed the title. I suspect it was a decision made by the new marketing staff.

The three components of the new *Math 65* third edition *Complete Package* include:

- A softcover student textbook.

- A softcover solutions manual that contains step-by-step solutions to the practice and mixed practice problems from the Daily Lessons, Investigations, Appendix Topics, the Supplemental Practice, the Facts Practice Tests, and the Tests.

- A softcover Tests and Worksheets Booklet that contains the Facts Practice Tests, the Activity Sheets, twenty-three tests, and the optional Recording Forms which can be photo-copied.

Neither the solutions manual nor the other support materials that come with the new third edition of *Math 65* are compatible with older second edition *Math 65* textbooks. These new third editions have been in print for a number of years and are also available in the used book marketplace. If parents buy one, make sure all three components are there and that all of the pages and tests are there as well.

Some parents may want the student to skip the first twenty or so lessons in *Math 65* because they appear to be like the last part of *Math 54*. Or, they may allow the student to skip the last twenty or so lessons, because they believe that material will be repeated in the early part of *Math 76*. Either of these shortcuts is likely to harm the student's ability to master the essential math concepts.

As I commented earlier in the book, one should not fall victim to the old rumor that these sections are only review and that students can move more quickly through the series if they skip one or both of these sections. What is the rush? Finish the entire textbook!

If students reach algebra one by the eighth grade, they will be in a calculus textbook their senior year and prepared for math at any university.

It is critical that the students are well-grounded in the basics of mathematics and that they have no conceptual weaknesses which have developed because they skipped over material.

Remember, it is confidence building for students to be able to review and use math concepts they are already familiar with. That is part of the process that develops mastery.

Mathematics is like swimming – or drowning! It is far easier to teach children how to swim in shallow water than to wait until they get into the deep water – over their heads. It is not possible to teach drowning children how to swim - while they are drowning!

Math 76

NOTE: Before reading this chapter, make sure you have read the foreword.

Math 76 is a sixth grade math textbook. It should be used following successful completion of *Math 65*. If students used *Math 65,* do not have them take the Saxon Middle Grade Placement Test to evaluate their progress for possible entry into this book. See the earlier chapter on *Student Placement*.

If students have just completed some other series fifth grade math program, they should also be placed in *Math 76*. Do not skip *Math 76* just because the early lessons in the textbook appear to repeat what students may have already studied.

If the parents do not know whether or not the students' previous non-Saxon course was a fifth or sixth grade math course, and they are considering skipping *Math 76*, they first should perform this simple evaluation.

Give students Test 22 from either the old hardcover third edition or the new softcover fourth edition of *Math 76*. Give them no more than forty-five minutes without a calculator and grade each problem as right or wrong. No partial credit! Students who receive a test score of eighty-five or better on that test can then safely move to either the second or third edition of either *Math 87* or *Algebra ½*.

The older hardcover third editions or the new softcover fourth editions of *Math 76* are the only two editions that should be used to successfully prepare the students for either *Math 87* or *Algebra ½*. The much older second edition of *Math 76* has been out of print for almost a decade, and, while an excellent sixth grade math book in its day, is considered academically weak by today's testing standards.

I love books, but if you have a copy of the much older old second edition of *Math 76*, I recommend you either throw it away or use it as a fourth or fifth grade supplemental book. Both the old hardcover third editions and the new softcover fourth editions of *Math 76* have lesson reference numbers and step-by-step test solutions.

While materials from the new fourth edition are not compatible with the older third edition textbooks, the difficulty and mathematical content of both editions remain almost identical.

There are a total of one hundred forty-four lessons in the older third edition of *Math 76*. Six of them are *Investigations*. The new softcover fourth edition has a total of one hundred thirty-two lessons, of which twelve are now identified as *Investigations*.

Specific differences between the two editions are itemized below.

1. Six of the lessons from the old third edition were converted to *Investigations* in the new fourth edition. These six were then added to the six already found in the old third edition, to create the twelve *Investigations* now found in the new fourth edition.

2. One *Additional Topic* was added at the end of the new fourth edition textbook. It is lesson 138 (Roman Numerals), taken from the older third edition textbook.

3. Ten lessons from the third edition were consolidated into other individual lessons in the fourth edition.

4. Tests were reduced from twenty-eight in the old third edition to twenty-three in the fourth edition.

5. A step-by-step solutions manual has been added to the new fourth edition.

In spite of these changes, the old hardcover third edition of *Math 76* is still an outstanding textbook that will prepare the student for either *Math 87* or *Algebra ½,* as we will discuss later.

The three components of the older third edition of *Math 76* were referred to by Saxon Publishers as the *Homeschool Kit.* The components include:

- A hardcover student textbook.

- A softcover Home Study Packet that contains the test solutions, answers to all the problems in the daily assignments, and answers to the Facts Practice Tests.

- A softcover Test Forms Booklet that contains the twenty-eight tests and the Facts Practice Test Forms.

If parents want to buy a used copy of the *Math 76* third edition, they should check to make sure that:

- All three components are there.

- All three have THIRD EDITION printed on the front covers.

- All of the pages and tests are inside the two booklets, as well as the testing schedule printed opposite Test 1.

Switching to the softcover was the idea of managers at the Saxon Publishers in Norman, Oklahoma. They wanted to add a solutions manual to the new middle grade *Math 54* to *Math 87* series, so they used soft covers to keep the price down.

The new fourth edition textbook of *Math 76* also has three components. But what Saxon Publishers referred to as the *Homeschool Kit* is now referred to as the *Complete Package.*

The three components of the new fourth edition of the *Math 76 Complete Package* include:

- A softcover student textbook.

- A softcover solutions manual that contains step-by-step solutions to the practice and mixed practice problems from the Daily Lessons, Investigations, Appendix Topics, the Supplemental Practice, the Facts Practice Tests, and the Tests.

- A softcover Tests and Worksheets Booklet that contains the Facts Practice Tests, the Activity Sheets, twenty-three tests, and the optional Recording Forms which can be photo-copied.

The solutions manual and the other support materials that come with the new fourth edition of *Math 76*, are not compatible with older editions of *Math 76*. These new softcover fourth editions have been in print for a number of years and are also now available in the used book marketplace. If you do buy one, make sure all three components are included, as well as all of their pages and tests.

Some parents may want the student to skip the first twenty or so lessons in the book because they appear to be like the last part of *Math 65*. Or, they may allow the student to skip the last twenty or so lessons, because they believe that material will be repeated in the early part of *Math 87*. Either of these shortcuts is likely to harm the student's ability to master the essential math concepts.

Either course of action will increase the student's difficulty in grasping the essential math concepts. As I commented earlier in the book, one should not fall victim to the rumor that these sections are only review, and that students can move quickly through the series by skipping one or both of these sections. What is the rush?

If students reach algebra one by the eighth grade, they will be in a calculus textbook their senior year and prepared for math at any university.

It is critical to make sure the student is well grounded in the basics of mathematics, and has no "holes" which have developed. Mathematics is like swimming – or drowning! It is far easier to teach children how to swim in shallow water than to wait until they get into the deep water – over their heads. It is not possible to teach drowning children how to swim - while they are drowning!

Successful completion of the third or fourth edition of *Math 76* means the student can proceed to either *Math 87*, second or third edition, or directly to the second or third edition of *Algebra ½*. Whether the student proceeds to *Math 87* or *Algebra ½* will depend upon their final five or six test scores in *Math 76*.

To successfully skip *Math 87* and move directly to *Algebra ½*, students must receive eighty or better on their last five or six tests in either the third or fourth edition of *Math 76*. This would be the score taken from their first time being tested.

As with any of the Saxon tests taken during the course, allow them no more than fifty minutes on each test without a calculator, and grade each problem as right or wrong. No partial credit!

Students who receive test scores of eighty or better can safely proceed to the second or third edition of *Algebra ½*. Students who cannot meet this criterion should proceed to either the second or third edition of *Math 87*.

Upon completion of *Math 87*, students can then proceed to either *Algebra ½* or directly to *Algebra 1,* depending on their performance. This will be discussed in more detail in the chapters discussing *Math 87* and *Algebra ½*.

If you went to the Saxon School Web site you might have noticed that there is a new sixth grade classroom textbook listed. It is titled *Saxon Math™ Course 1.*

The cover of the textbook has a picture of a soccer ball on the cover. *Course 1* contains the same content as the fourth edition of *Math 76.*

Because state textbook review committees have little time or ability to read every textbook they are considering for adoption, publishers added highlighted comments so members of these review committees could easily see what is in each lesson.

I would call the other changes in these new textbooks nothing more than just *cosmetic bells and whistles,* to also make it easier for teachers to meet their mandated state reporting requirements.

The highlights, notes, and other comments provided in this new textbook are neither useful nor required by homeschool parents. If a homeschool version of this is released in the future, specifics about it will be provided in the on-line advisory *Homeschool Newsletter* at *www.homeschoolwithsaxon.com.*

Unless, however, the publisher makes substantial conceptual changes, I would not recommend homeschool families attempt to use *Course 1* at this time.

Math 87

NOTE: Before reading this chapter, make sure you have read the foreword.

Math 87 is a seventh grade textbook. In John Saxon's original math series, it was to be used by students after they had successfully completed *Math 76*. Upon completion of the older *Math 87* editions, students then went on to use *Algebra ½*. The strength of the newer editions of both *Math 76* and *Math 87*, however, has afforded students other options. These will be discussed later in this chapter.

The older first edition of *Math 87* has been out of print for almost a decade and, while an excellent seventh grade math book in its time, would now be considered academically weak for a seventh grade math book. I would not recommend using it as a preparatory text for *Algebra 1*. If it is used, the student should then proceed to the *Algebra ½* textbook before attempting *Algebra 1*.

The second edition of *Math 87* is also out of print; the older hardback second editions, as well as the new softcover third editions of *Math 87*, however, are still excellent pre-algebra math textbooks. Both of these editions do an excellent job of preparing students for any algebra one course.

Students who have completed some other series sixth grade math program should be placed in either *Math 87* or *Algebra ½* before attempting *Algebra 1*. The contents of both books may appear to be the same; however; *Math 87* starts off with a review of some sixth grade concepts. *Algebra ½* does not have this review.

Math 87 would be more appropriate for a student who needs additional review based on concept difficulties reflected by low sixth grade test scores.

One reason why *Math 87* contains the daily Facts Practice at the beginning of each lesson, while *Algebra ½* does not, is that students using *Math 87* generally require this additional drill; however, those students who do not need this type of review can skip these daily drills and proceed directly to the daily problems in the lesson.

Before placing a non-Saxon student directly into either *Math 87* or *Algebra ½*, parents should have the student take the Saxon Middle Grade Placement Test. If the results of that test do not clearly indicate the student should be in *Math 87*, then parents should perform this simple evaluation.

Give the student Test 23 from either the older hardcover third edition or the new softcover fourth edition of *Math 76*. Allow the student no more than forty-five minutes to take the test, without a calculator. Grade each problem right or wrong. No partial credit!

Students receiving test scores of eighty or better on this test can be confidently placed in *Algebra ½*. Lower test results would indicate they should start with *Math 87*.

As with *Math 76* discussed earlier, there are only two editions of *Math 87* that homeschool parents should consider using for seventh grade students. They are the older hardcover second edition and the new softcover third edition.

Even though the older hardcover second edition of *Math 87* has been out of print for several years, it is still an excellent textbook to use in preparing students for any algebra one course.

My analysis of the two books reveals there are very few changes between them. Both the older hardcover second editions and the new softcover third editions of *Math 87* have lesson reference numbers and step-by-step solutions to the tests.

Their specific differences are listed below.

1. The new third edition textbook added the phrase *with Pre-algebra* under the book's title on the front cover.

2. The problems dealing with the concepts of *Some and Some More* and *Some Went Away* found in the second edition were renamed *Combining* and *Separating* problems in the new third edition.

3. Three pages were added as *Topic A* at the end of the new third edition. These pages contain information on *Base 2* and *Roman Numerals*.

4. The Final Exam, found in the second edition, was dropped from the new third edition. The number of tests remains at twenty-three in both editions. Since all tests are cumulative, the final exam was not really necessary.

5. A step-by-step solutions manual was added to the new third edition.

NOTE: Because of the identical content of these two editions, the new third edition solutions manual can be used with the older second edition textbook. I recommend buying a used second edition Homeschool Kit with the hard cover textbook and then buying a third edition solutions manual.

The three components of the older second editions of *Math 87* were originally referred to by Saxon Publishers as the *Homeschool Kit.* These three components include:

- A hardcover student textbook.

- A softcover Home Study Packet that contains the test solutions answers to all the problems in the daily assignments, and answers to the Facts Practice Tests.

- A softcover Test Forms Booklet that contains the twenty-eight tests and the Facts Practice Test Forms.

If parents want to buy a used copy of the older hardback second edition of *Math 87*, they should check to make sure that:

- All three components are there.

- All three have SECOND EDITION printed on the front covers.

- All of the pages and tests are inside the two booklets, as well as the testing schedule printed opposite Test 1.

Switching to the softcover was a decision made by managers at the original Saxon Publishers. They wanted to add a solutions manual to the new middle grade math series for *Math 54* through *Math 87,* so they used soft covers to keep the price down.

The new third edition of *Math 87* also has three components. But what Saxon Publishers previously called the *Homeschool Kit* is now referred to as the *Complete Package.* The three components of the *Complete Package* include:

- A softcover student textbook.

- A softcover solutions manual that contains step-by-step solutions to the practice and mixed practice problems from the Daily Lessons, Investigations, Appendix Topics, the Supplemental Practice, Facts Practice Tests, and the Tests.

- A softcover Tests and Worksheets Booklet that contains the Facts Practice Tests, the Activity Sheets, twenty-three tests, and the optional Recording Forms which can be photo-copied.

These new third editions have been in print for a number of years and are also available in the used book marketplace. If parents buy them, make sure all three components are there and that all of the pages and tests are there as well.

Some parents may want the student to skip the first twenty or so lessons in the book because they appear to be like the last part of *Math 76*. Or, they may allow the student to skip the last twenty or so lessons, because they believe that material will be repeated in the early part of *Algebra 1*. Either of these shortcuts is likely to harm the student's ability to master the essential math concepts.

As I commented earlier in the book, one should not fall victim to the rumor that these sections are only review and that students can move quickly through the series by skipping one or both of these sections.

What is the rush? If students reach algebra one by the eighth grade, they will be in a calculus textbook their senior year and prepared for math at any university.

Mathematics is like swimming – or drowning! It is far easier to teach children how to swim in shallow water than to wait until they get into the deep water – over their heads. It is not possible to teach drowning children how to swim - while they are drowning!

As we said earlier, some students master math concepts faster than others. Students who struggle through the last five or six tests in *Math 87*, receiving test scores below seventy-five, should proceed to *Algebra ½* rather than attempting *Algebra 1*.

While the material in *Algebra ½* is basically the same as *Math 87,* using that textbook is not like repeating the same math book. Students will receive another chance to master the same material from a different perspective. This will increase their confidence, as well as their abilities to be successful in any algebra one textbook.

If you went to the Saxon School Web site, you might have noticed there is a new seventh grade classroom textbook listed. It is titled *Saxon Math™ Course 2.* The cover of the textbook has a picture of a pair of binoculars on the cover. *Course 2* contains the same content as the third edition of *Math 87.*

Because state textbook review committees have little time or ability to read every textbook they are considering for adoption, publishers added highlighted comments so members of these review committees could easily see what was in each lesson.

I would call the other changes in this new textbook nothing more than just *cosmetic bells and whistles* to also make it easier for teachers to meet their mandated reporting requirements. The highlights, notes, and other comments provided in this new textbook are neither useful nor required by homeschool parents.

If a homeschool version of this is released in the future, specifics about it will be provided in the on-line advisory *Homeschool Newsletter* at *www.homeschoolwithsaxon.com.*

Unless the publishers make substantial conceptual changes, however, I would not recommend homeschool families attempt using *Course 2* at this time.

Algebra ½

Algebra ½ can be used as either a seventh or eighth grade textbook. It is what other publishers refer to as a pre-algebra textbook, preparing the student for algebra.

The content of this book is almost identical to that of *Math 87.* This book, however, does not have the sixth grade math review at the beginning of the book that *Math 87* has; nor does it have the familiar "Warm-Up-Box" at the beginning of each lesson. Success in either book prepares students for *Algebra 1.*

Beginning with this textbook, tests are now scheduled every four lessons. Students now work a separate lesson Monday through Thursday and take a test every Friday – with no week-end assignment to do!

In John Saxon's original math series, this book was used by students after they had completed *Math 87.* Upon completion of older *Math 87* editions, students went on to use this textbook as preparation for *Algebra 1.* The strength of the newer editions of both *Math 76* and *Math 87,* however, has afforded students other options. These options were discussed in the preceding chapters dealing with those specific textbooks.

The two useable editions of *Algebra ½* are the older second and the newer third editions. Both editions have hardcover textbooks. While the older second edition has been out of print for several years, it is still a good edition to use as long as you have all of the components. They are no longer available from Saxon.

The specific differences between them will be discussed later, but mastery of the content of either edition will prepare the student for *Algebra 1.* There is a much older first edition of *Algebra ½*; it has, however, been out of print for more than a decade.

This much older first edition was a good book in its day, but stronger mandated academic standards have rendered it an academically weak book for seventh or eighth grade use today. As I mentioned earlier, I love books, but if you have a copy of the old first edition of *Algebra ½* (circa 1983), I recommend you either throw it away or use it as a sixth grade supplemental.

To be successful in *Algebra ½*, students who struggle with mathematics should have satisfactorily completed all of the lessons in *Math 87*, second edition, or the new softcover third edition textbook. Or, if they are unusually strong math students, they should have successfully mastered the entirety of the third edition, or the new softcover fourth edition of *Math 76*, based upon the academic criteria described in the earlier chapter on *Math 76*.

Students who have completed a non-Saxon series sixth or seventh grade math program should not be placed in this textbook until they have first taken the Saxon Middle Grade Placement Test. Parents should either give students that test or perform this evaluation.

Give the students Test 15 from either the hardcover third edition or new softcover fourth edition of *Math 76*. Give them no more than forty-five minutes without a calculator and grade each problem as right or wrong. No partial credit! If the students receive a test score of less than eighty on that test, they should be placed in *Math 87*.

If, however, they receive a test score of eighty or better, they then should be given Test 22. If they receive a test score of eighty or better on that test, they can then safely start in *Algebra ½*.

Receiving a score well below that indicates they should begin in either *Math 87* or *Math 76*, depending upon their scores. Follow the procedures discussed in the previous chapters dealing with *Math 76* and *Math 87* to see where to successfully start students.

While materials from the new third edition are not compatible with the older second edition textbooks, the difficulty and mathematical content of both editions remain almost identical.

One of the major differences between these two editions is that the new third edition has both test solutions and lesson reference numbers. The older second edition has neither.

There are one hundred thirty-seven lessons in the second edition of *Algebra ½,* with no additional topics. The new third edition has only one hundred twenty-three lessons, but there are ten *Additional Topics* printed after lesson one hundred twenty-three.

These *Additional Topics* found in the new third edition should be covered in conjunction with other lessons found earlier in the textbook. When I taught using this textbook, I combined them with the following lessons.

TOPIC	LESSON	TOPIC	LESSON
A	9 or 98	F	94, 101, or 102
B	29	G	115
C	4 or 106	H	85
D	64	I	85
E	117	J	117

You may choose different lessons to associate these additional topics with, or you may choose to skip them, depending upon the situation and the child's abilities.

In spite of these changes, the old second edition is still an outstanding textbook that will prepare the student for *Algebra 1* just as well as the new third edition does.

The three components of the older second edition of *Algebra 1/2* were originally referred to by Saxon Publishers as the *Homeschool Kit*. They include:

- A hardcover student textbook that contains answers to only the odd numbered problems.

- A softcover booklet titled the Home Study Packet that contains answers to both the weekly tests, as well as all the problems in the daily assignments.

- A softcover booklet titled Test Forms that contains thirty-four tests, a final exam, and a testing schedule.

There was also a softcover solutions manual containing step-by-step solutions to every problem in the textbook. The solutions manual was sold separately.

If parents want to buy a used copy of the older second edition of the *Algebra ½* Homeschool Kit, they should make sure that:

- All three components are there.

- All three of them have SECOND EDITION printed on their covers.

- All of the pages and tests are inside the two booklets, as well as the testing schedule printed opposite Test 1.

The new third edition of *Algebra ½* also has three components. But what Saxon Publishers used to refer to as the *Homeschool Kit* is now referred to as the *Complete Package*. The three components include:

- A hardcover student textbook that also contains answers to only the odd numbered problems.

- A softcover booklet titled the Homeschool Packet that contains solutions to the weekly tests and answers to all the problems in the daily assignments.

- A softcover booklet titled Test Forms containing thirty-one tests and a testing schedule.

Since all *Algebra ½* tests are cumulative tests, the final exam used in the older second edition was removed from the new third edition as an unnecessary testing requirement.

There is also a softcover solutions manual containing step-by-step solutions to every problem in the textbook. The solutions manual is sold separately. The manual and the other support materials that come with the new third edition of *Algebra ½,* are not compatible with older editions of the *Algebra ½* textbooks.

These new third editions have been in print for a number of years and are also now available in the used book marketplace. If you buy them, make sure all three components are included, as well as all of their pages and tests.

Some parents may want the student to skip the first twenty or so lessons in this course because they appear to be like those in the last part of *Math 76* or *Math 87*. Or, they may allow the student to skip the last twenty or so lessons, because they believe that material will be repeated in the early part of *Algebra 1*. Either of these shortcuts is likely to harm the student's ability to master the essential math concepts.

As I commented earlier in the book, parents should not fall victim to the false idea that these sections are only review and that the student can move quickly through the series by skipping one or both of these sections.

Parents should not take either of these shortcuts. Students need the review and reinforcement. Why rush the student?

If students reach *Algebra 1* by the eighth grade, they will be studying calculus their senior year and they will be prepared for freshman mathematics at any university. It is critical to make sure the student is well grounded in the basics of mathematics and has not developed holes in his math background.

Studying mathematics is like swimming – or drowning! It is far easier to teach children how to swim in shallow water than to wait until they get into the deep water – over their heads. It is not possible to teach drowning children how to swim – while they are drowning!

Successful completion of all of the lessons in the second or third edition of *Algebra ½* means the student can then safely proceed to *Algebra 1*, having mastered rather than memorized the essential math concepts.

If you went to the Saxon School Web site, you might have noticed there is a new textbook titled *Saxon Math™ Course 3*. The cover of the textbook has a picture of a violin on the cover. *Course 3* contains much of the same content found in the new third edition of *Algebra ½*, as well as some *Algebra 1* and *Algebra 2* content.

The highlights, notes, and other comments provided in this new textbook are neither useful nor required by homeschool parents. If a homeschool version of this is released in the future, specifics about it will be provided in the on-line advisory *Homeschool Newsletter* at *www.homeschoolwithsaxon.com*.

Unless they make substantial conceptual changes in the future, I would not recommend using *Course 3* at home at this time.

Two Textbooks – Four Years

Regardless of how well students may do in literature, history or social sciences, some still struggle with mathematics. Their struggle generally starts with *Algebra ½* or *Algebra 1*, and unless the problems are resolved, it continues into *Algebra 2*, defeating their hopes for success in college math and science.

Most students who encounter difficulties in *Algebra 1* or *Algebra 2* do so because of one or two reasons. Either they are not completely prepared for the subject material from their previous math courses of instruction, or they are unable to handle both the algebra and the geometry contained in these textbooks – or both!

Using *Algebra 1* and *Algebra 2* as four separate math courses by applying the concept of **lesser inclusive credit** is an idea recommended by the author and approved by the Oklahoma State Board of Education in 1992. The procedures are still used by some private and public schools (using Saxon math books) in the states of Kansas, Oklahoma, Arkansas, Missouri, New Mexico, Texas, and Colorado.

Today many high schools use a variation of this process by teaching *Algebra 1A* and *Algebra 1B* or *Algebra 2A* and *Algebra 2B*. However, rather than challenging students, what these courses do is take a full year to teach the first half of the textbook and another full year to finish the second half of the same textbook.

Teachers and administrators who use this technique believe that by slowing down the instruction, the slower students can absorb the material more readily and maintain a passing grade.

But like the course outlines of old, the teacher still must pass out review sheets before the monthly tests, and that technique reinforces the process of memory rather than mastery.

Both my military and my teaching experiences have shown me that slowing down expectations eventually leads to reduced efforts by the participants, whether they are soldiers or students.

It is difficult to determine which students will encounter problems with an algebra course, regardless of their previous level of instruction or academic grades in those courses.

Circumstances beyond the control of parents or teachers often come into play in the middle of a school year or grading period. These circumstances may affect a student's performance after he has apparently done well in the preceding math courses.

Most students are enrolled in *Algebra 1* by the time they are in their freshman year of high school. In my previous school district, we had two types of math students. One group took *Algebra ½* in the seventh grade and *Algebra 1* in the eighth grade. These students were taking *Algebra 2* their freshman year of high school.

The other group was students who took *Algebra ½* in the eighth grade and *Algebra 1* their freshman year. However, the concept of awarding lesser inclusive credit would hold true for students encountering difficulty in *Algebra 1* at any grade level.

When students encounter difficulty in *Algebra 1,* it will be reflected by their test grades falling below an overall C average. This generally appears after lesson thirty in the textbook or by the end of the first nine week period.

Because of the cumulative nature of the textbook, the rest of the book does not get any easier. Students generally end up with even lower test scores as they proceed through the textbook, unless something is done to correct the problem before they actually start to receive failing test grades.

When this situation occurs while the students are taking *Algebra 1*, their transcript should be changed to reflect the lesser inclusive credit titled *Basic Algebra.*

Students remain in the *Algebra 1* class, and they should still attempt the material as presented in the remainder of the textbook; they are now graded, however, on a ***lesser included grading scale***. Instead of using the regular 90, 80, 70, 60 grading scale, their tests are now scored on a 75, 65, 55, and 45 scale.

This revised grading scale, when applied against the remaining tests, reflects the lesser inclusive grade for the *Basic Algebra* course now reflected on their transcript. The first nine weeks' grade is also adjusted to reflect the new grade based upon this revised grading scale.

*EXAMPLE: A student is receiving test scores of seventy or lower near the end of the first nine weeks of Algebra 1. He is experiencing difficulty in mastering all of the new material being presented in the book. The student's transcript would be changed from **Algebra 1** to show the new course titled **Basic Algebra.***

*The student's first nine week's grade of C (a 75 average) would be changed to reflect a new grade of an A based upon the new grading scale for the lesser inclusive course of **Basic Algebra.***

The student then continues in the same Algebra 1 book. He continues to do all of the lessons and all of the problems as best he can. However, the tests are now scored on the new grading scale.

*Therefore, continued test scores of sixty-five would receive a grade of B while scores of sixty would be recorded as a B-, etc. The grades would be recorded for the new lesser inclusive course titled **Basic Algebra.***

The following year, the student would retake Algebra 1 using the same Algebra 1 textbook. He would then receive credit for Algebra 1.

In the ten years that we used this system in our school, more than ninety-five percent of the hundreds of students in the program received either a final grade of A or B their second year in *Algebra 1.*

The other few students who did not really apply themselves received grades of B's and C's. I can count on one hand the number of students who received a grade of D or less.

This same process can be applied to students encountering difficulties in *Algebra 2.* They would have the new title of *Introduction to Algebra 2* entered on their transcripts. The students would then remain in *Algebra 2* for the remainder of the school year.

They would continue doing the assignments presented in the remainder of *Algebra 2*, but these students would also be graded on the lesser included grading scale, as we discussed above, for the *Algebra 1* student who encountered difficulty.

The following year these students then repeat the course using the same textbook. The second year *Algebra 2* is entered on their transcript. Again, ninety percent or more do exceptionally well given this second opportunity.

Using this technique, the high school where I taught raised math ACT scores from 13.4 to 21.9 (above the National Average) in a three-year period. The school also "tripled" the number of high school students taking the ACT test, and they increased the number of high school students in math classes above *Algebra 1* to more than "ninety percent"! More students were also becoming eligible to attend colleges and universities.

Sometimes the difficulty students encounter in *Algebra 1* or *Algebra 2* stems from their inability to process both the algebra and the geometry concepts at the same time. Some students just need a second or third chance to master this material because of their weaker math background in pre-algebra. Or, they might have transferred in from another math series and they had not previously been exposed to any geometry.

What makes the concept work so well is that *Algebra 1* and *Algebra 2* are really tough, no-nonsense, cumulative textbooks. Using this system, we have shown that any student who truly masters the content of these two textbooks in four years of high school will successfully pass any college level algebra course at any university.

Some of my colleagues at the high school were concerned at first that we were giving the students easy grades. Yes, the students were given a second and sometimes a third chance to learn the material because they needed them!

Aside from that, participating students were not given anything except what they earned. The student who sits and does nothing in any of the classes receives his just reward, as in any academic situation.

In the ten years we used this program, I never met students or parents who, when the program was properly explained to them, did not look positively upon the program as a second or sometimes third, chance to master the necessary concepts of algebra.

Algebra 1

John Saxon would often remark that "algebra is not difficult, it is just different." He felt it was mastery of the basics that created the capability for critical thinking and not the other way around.

He would really get agitated whenever he encountered a math teacher who would go on about how they were teaching "critical thinking" to their seventh and eighth grade math students rather than the repetitive basics they thought would bore the students.

The educator who believes that critical or higher-order thinking is more important than first understanding and applying the basics in the seventh and eighth grades is doomed to get hit by the falling piano.

If I were standing alongside one of these so called "educators" looking up at the 23d floor of a high rise building, and we both saw a piano falling on us, I would immediately get out from under the falling object.

He, using his learned critical thinking skills, of course, would stand there under the falling piano, contemplating the origin of the effects of its rapid descent, trying to determine from its velocity and position in space if it were pushed or rolled off the balcony!

Any young algebra student who has not mastered decimals, fractions and percents will encounter extreme difficulty, if not failure, in algebra class. I remember my high school principal telling me, "You're the math teacher; you teach them how." I explained to him that I could not do that. The students were drowning, and I could not teach them how to swim while they were drowning.

I went on to explain to him that if I were to slow the course down and try to teach these students what they had not learned in the fourth, fifth or sixth grade math classes, I would not finish the book. The remainder of the students would then suffer because they would then not be prepared for *Algebra 2*.

It was the discovery of these conditions, uncovered by use of John Saxon's math books, that demanded the school district adopt the plan for using two textbooks over the four years of high school, which was discussed in the previous chapter.

Our school administration and Board of Education had discovered previous math teachers had been masking the problem by using the old technique of reviewing for tests, or as I would tell them, "They had been painting the rust!"

It took a while, but we finally got Board of Education and the school administration to see that when students enter the world of algebra, they must be armed with the right weaponry – they must be able to swim in the deep water!

Algebra 1 should follow successful completion of *Algebra ½* or some other pre-algebra course. While *Algebra 1* is normally taken in the eighth or ninth grade, the reading level of *Algebra 1* will allow using it in the seventh grade provided students have first satisfactorily completed a pre-algebra course.

The current edition of *Algebra 1* is the third edition. While there may still be some older second edition books out there, that particular edition has been out of print for a number of years and materials for it are no longer available from Saxon.

While the older second edition of *Algebra 1* will also prepare the student for *Algebra 2*, the newer third edition has been academically strengthened to keep up with changing testing standards.

The third edition has test solutions as well as the lesson reference numbers, neither of which are found in the older second edition. Support materials from the new third edition are not compatible with the older second edition textbooks.

Students who have completed some other non-Saxon series pre-algebra math program should not be placed in this textbook until they have first taken the Saxon Placement Test.

If it cannot be determined whether or not the students' previous non-Saxon math course was a strong pre-algebra math program, parents should either give them the Saxon Placement Test for *Algebra 1* or perform this evaluation first.

Give the students Test 20 from either the second or third editions of *Math 87* or *Algebra ½*. Give them no more than fifty minutes without a calculator and grade each problem as right or wrong. No partial credit!

If the students receive a test score of eighty or better, they can then safely start in this textbook. However, if students score below an eighty, have them start in the second or third editions of either *Math 87*, or *Algebra ½*.

The worst thing that will happen is that in the early twenty or so lessons of those books, the student may scream like a wounded duck that "This is too easy!" However, since we do not know where all the holes are, we cannot skip or fish around.

Tell the students if it is that easy, it won't take them long to do their homework! Tell them to be patient; the content will get more difficult very soon! But do not acquiesce to their demands. They need to gain their confidence back, as well as fill in the holes in their math background developed over the previous several years.

By doing the early thirty or so lessons of either of these books, students will rebuild their confidence and strengthen the parts of their math background that are weak. Careful, methodical study of these lessons will prevent them from later stumbling in Algebra *2*.

There are three review lessons and one hundred thirty-five regular lessons in the older second edition of algebra one. The new third edition has only one hundred twenty lessons.

The three components of the second edition of *Algebra 1* were originally referred to by Saxon Publishers as the *Homeschool Kit.* They include:

- A hardcover student textbook that also contains answers to only the odd numbered problems.

- A softcover booklet titled the Home Study Packet that contains answers to both the weekly tests and all the problems in the daily assignments.

- A softcover booklet titled Test Forms that contains thirty-four tests, a final exam, and a testing schedule.

There is also a softcover solutions manual containing step-by-step solutions to every problem in the textbook. The solutions manual was sold separately. If parents want to buy a used copy of the second edition of *Algebra 1,* they should make sure that:

- All three components are there.

- All three of them have SECOND EDITION printed on their covers.

- All of the pages and tests are inside the two booklets, as well as the testing schedule printed opposite Test 1.

The new third edition of *Algebra 1* also has three components. But what Saxon Publishers used to call the *Homeschool Kit* is now referred to as the *Complete Package*. The components include:

- A hardcover student textbook book that also contains answers to only the odd numbered problems.

- A softcover booklet titled the Homeschool Packet that contains solutions to the weekly tests and answers to all the problems in the daily assignments.

- A softcover booklet titled Test Forms containing thirty tests and a testing schedule.

Since all *Algebra 1* tests are cumulative tests, the final exam used in the second edition was removed from the new third edition as an unnecessary testing requirement.

There is also a softcover solutions manual containing step-by-step solutions to every problem in the textbook. The solutions manual is sold separately. The solutions manual and the other support materials that come with the new third edition of *Algebra 1*, are not compatible with older editions of *Algebra 1.*

Some parents may want the student to skip the first twenty or so lessons in this course because they appear to contain the same material as those in the last part of *Math 87* or *Algebra ½*. Or, they may allow the student to skip the last twenty or so lessons, because they believe that material will be repeated in the early part of *Algebra 2.* Either of these shortcuts is likely to harm the student's ability to master the essential math concepts.

But as I commented earlier, parents should not fall victim to this age old rumor that these sections are only review and that a student can move quickly through the series by skipping one or both of these sections.

At this level of mathematics, either choice would be disastrous for the average student. Besides, what is the rush? It is critical to make sure the student is well-grounded in the basics of mathematics and has no "holes" which have developed. Mathematics is like swimming – or drowning!

Again, it is far easier to teach children how to swim in shallow water than to wait until they get into the deep water – over their heads. It is not possible to teach drowning children how to swim - while they are drowning!

Avoid taking shortcuts!

Algebra 2

Algebra 2 is to be used after the student successfully completes either the second or third edition of *Algebra 1*. Mastery of the concepts presented in this textbook, without going any further in high school mathematics, will prepare the student for success in any credited freshman college algebra course from MIT to Stanford!

From the very start of this textbook, it is assumed that the student has already mastered the concepts of an algebra one course, as well as having been exposed to an introduction to basic geometry.

To be successful in this textbook, the students should have finished *Algebra 1* in its entirety. Their last five or six test scores in *Algebra 1* should have been eighty or better.

Students who experience difficulty in this book by the time they reach lesson twenty or so can most likely attribute their difficulties to one or more of the following reasons.

- They skipped *Algebra 1* or used a weaker non-Saxon textbook meant for pre-algebra use.

- They did not complete the entirety of *Algebra 1,* or they rushed through the book doing only half the problems in each lesson.

- Their last five or six tests in *Algebra 1* were all below a seventy-five.

- They never took the weekly tests in *Algebra 1* to determine mastery of those concepts.

- They took a separate geometry course after completing *Algebra 1* and have forgotten many of those concepts, having now been away from *Algebra 1* for almost fifteen months (nine regular school months plus two summer sessions).

Students transferring from another math series or a non-Saxon algebra one textbook should first take the *Saxon Algebra 2 Placement Test* to determine if they would be successful in *Algebra 2*.

The placement test can be found on the Saxon Homeschool Web site. For students who do not satisfactorily pass that placement test, parents should consider having them test through *Algebra 1* to see where in that textbook they should start.

To successfully test through *Algebra 1*, start with Test 5. There is no reason to waste time testing in any earlier test unless the students fail that test. Give students fifty minutes to complete the test, not a minute more! A calculator may be used.

When grading these tests, do not award any partial credit. The answers should be scored as either right or wrong. If the students receive an eighty or better on test five, then have them review the lessons dealing with the problems that they answered incorrectly that same day before moving to the next test.

The next day have them take Test 10, repeating this process over the next few days until students either test out of *Algebra 1*, or until they receive two test scores in a row below eighty.

When students receive two test scores in a row below an eighty, that is where they start in *Algebra 1*. If necessary, have them take one more test to confirm that their test scores are dropping. They should then back up five lessons and finish the rest of *Algebra 1* before starting *Algebra 2*.

Upon satisfactory completion of the entirety of *Algebra 2*, in addition to a full year's credit for *Algebra 2*, the student will also have completed the equivalent of the first semester of a high school geometry course. More details are provided in the chapter titled *Geometry Credit* later in the book.

Because of the increasing number of standard formulas to use in both this textbook and the next one (*Advanced Mathematics*), I let my classroom students use 4 x 6 inch formula cards. You might try letting your student use them.

The front of the card would show the title of the formula, for example, *Area of a Sector*. Then on the back of the card in the upper right hand corner, they would record the page on which that formula was found (page 19 in the 2d Ed and page 16 in the new 3d Ed).

In the center of the card on the back side under the page reference number, they would record the printed formula as it was found in the textbook. The page reference number on the card is beneficial to students when they want to go back later to review specific information dealing with using that formula. Students can use these cards while doing their daily work, as well as using them on their weekly tests. It will save them valuable study time now wasted looking through the book for the formulas.

It is also another way to create mastery of the individual formulas without constantly telling students they have to memorize them. If you watch them over a period of time, you will observe they master the formulas a lot quicker, knowing they have access to them if they forget.

The current edition of *Algebra 2* is the third edition. However, the only differences between the new third edition and the older second edition are that the new third edition has added lesson reference numbers and step-by-step solutions to the individual test questions.

There are two review lessons and one hundred twenty-nine other lessons in both the older second edition and the new third edition of *Algebra 2*. The number of pages was reduced from 603 pages in the second edition to 588 pages in the new third edition because of the different size margins, spacing, and graphics used in the new third edition textbook.

The three components of the second edition of *Algebra 2* were originally referred to by Saxon Publishers as the *Homeschool Kit.* The components include:

- A hardcover student textbook that also contains answers to only the odd numbered problems.

- A softcover booklet titled the Home Study Packet that contains answers to the weekly tests, and answers to all the problems in the daily assignments.

- A softcover booklet titled Test Forms that contains a testing schedule, thirty-two tests, and a final exam.

There is also a softcover solutions manual containing step-by-step solutions to every problem in the textbook. The solutions manual was sold separately. If parents want to buy a used copy of the second edition of *Algebra 2*, they should make sure that:

- All three components are there.

- All three of them have SECOND EDITION printed on their covers.

- All of the pages and tests are inside the two booklets, as well as the testing schedule printed opposite Test 1.

The new third edition of *Algebra 2* is still referred to as the *Homeschool Kit* and it also has three components. They include:

- A hardcover student textbook book that also contains answers to only the odd numbered problems.

- A softcover booklet titled ***Answer Key*** that contains only the answers to problems in the daily assignments.

- A softcover booklet titled **Homeschool Testing Book** containing the testing schedule, thirty-two tests, and step-by-step solutions to the test questions.

Since all *Algebra 2* tests are cumulative tests, the final exam used in the older second edition was removed from the new third edition test booklet as an unnecessary requirement. There is also a solutions manual containing step-by-step solutions to every problem in the textbook. The solutions manual is sold separately.

When the new third edition was released in late 2006, the publishing company also offered the Homeschool Kit with the solutions manual. The Kit with the solutions manual sells for a few dollars less than if the manual was purchased separately.

Parents may want the student to skip the first twenty or so lessons in this course because they appear to be like those in the last part of Algebra 1. Or, they may allow the student to skip the last twenty or so lessons, because they believe that material will be repeated in the early part of *Advanced Mathematics.* Either of these shortcuts is likely to harm the student's ability to master the essential math concepts.

At this level of mathematics, either choice would be disastrous for a student. Parents should not fall victim to the false idea that these sections are only review and that students can move quickly through the series by skipping one or both of these sections.

Advanced Mathematics

The second edition of *Advanced Mathematics* is a precalculus textbook that should be used after successful completion of the entirety of the second or third editions of *Algebra 2.*

There is a much older book titled *Geometry-Trigonometry-Algebra II* that has been out of print for more than fifteen years. If you have a copy of that book, save it as a collector's item, but do not use it as a precalculus textbook.

There is also an older first edition of *Advanced Mathematics* that has also been out of print for almost a decade now; it is, however, still circulating among used book sources. The current second edition is better organized and is academically stronger than the older first edition.

The second edition of *Advanced Mathematics* also contains the equivalent of the second semester of a high school geometry course. Students complete the equivalent of their first semester of high school geometry when they finish *Algebra 2.*

The second edition of *Advanced Mathematics* has added the test solutions, as well as the lesson reference numbers to both the tests and the daily problems. However, unlike the other Saxon textbooks which have the lesson reference numbers printed in parenthesis under the individual problem number, the lesson reference numbers in the second edition of *Advanced Mathematics* are found in the solutions manual and not in the textbook itself.

The contents of the second edition of *Advanced Mathematics* are more rigorous than most freshman college algebra/trigonometry courses, and the textbook should not be attempted in a single school year of nine months.

I have known only one student to successfully complete the entire textbook with an A average in a single nine-month school year. She was a National Merit Scholar and her father taught mathematics with me at the local university.

While John Saxon originally meant for the textbook to be taken as a three semester course, I successfully used it as a four-semester course for more than a dozen years in the rural high school where I taught.

I would strongly recommend that parents of homeschool students do the same to prevent creating undue pressure on the young student. Having three to four hours or more of challenging daily work in this textbook, while holding down a job or being involved in other activities and academic courses, puts a tremendous burden upon the student.

Before I discuss the specifics on how to use the book over a four-semester, two-year course, let me first discuss the contents of the Homeschool Kit. The three components of the first edition of *Advanced Mathematics* were originally referred to by Saxon Publishers as the *Homeschool Kit.* They include:

- A hardcover student textbook that contains answers to only the odd numbered problems.

- A softcover booklet titled *Home Study Packet* that contains the testing schedule, thirty-two tests, and the test answers.

- A softcover booklet titled *Teachers Edition Answers.* That contains only answers to the textbook problems.

There was also a softcover solutions manual containing step-by-step solutions to every problem in the textbook. The solutions manual was sold separately.

If parents want to buy a used copy of the first edition of *Advanced Mathematics*, they should make sure that:

- All three components are there.

- All of the pages and tests are inside the two booklets, as well as the testing schedule printed opposite Test 1.

Note: First edition materials did not have FIRST EDITION printed on their front covers.

The new second edition of *Advanced Mathematics* is now referred to as the *Complete Package* and it also has three components. They include:

- A hardcover student textbook that also contains answers to only the odd numbered problems.

- A softcover booklet titled the Home Study Packet that contains step-by-step solutions to the individual test questions and answers to all the problems found in the daily assignments.

- A softcover booklet titled Test Forms that contains a testing schedule and copies of the thirty-one tests.

There is also a softcover solutions manual containing step-by-step solutions to every problem in the textbook. The solutions manual is sold separately.

Whether you acquire it new or used, parents will want to have the solutions manual because that is where the lesson reference numbers for the daily problems are located.

Parents may want the student to skip the first twenty or so lessons in this course because they appear to be like those in the last part of *Algebra 2*.

Or, they may not want the student to finish the book, skipping the last fifteen or so lessons because they believe that material will be repeated in the early part of *Calculus*.

As I have commented earlier in the book, do not fall victim to the old rumor that these sections are only review and that the student can move more quickly through the series by skipping one or both of these sections. At this level of mathematics, either of these choices would be disastrous for the average student.

Here is a detailed outline for using the Advanced Mathematics textbook over four semesters or two years.

The first year students use Advanced Mathematics, they should plan to go through lesson ninety. They should take two days for each lesson.

They should do the odd numbered problems the first day and the even numbered problems the second day. This system permits the student time to complete all concepts both days since the problems generally come in pairs.

Attempting to do problems one through fifteen the first day and sixteen through thirty the second day will not work as that gives the student an uneven daily task and leaves several days between some of the individual concepts being reviewed.

The tests would normally occur every four lessons as they did in Algebra 1 and Algebra 2; however, because the lessons are now split over two days, the tests will now occur every eight days rather than four. After completing the first ninety lessons, the student's transcript should reflect either Geometry or Geometry with Advanced Algebra. Specific details are discussed in the next chapter.

In the second year in Advanced Mathematics, students step back and start with lesson sixty. They repeat lessons sixty through ninety. Parents invariably ask why the students repeat these thirty lessons but not others in this textbook.

The material that the students encountered in these thirty or so lessons contains, among other trigonometric concepts, half-angle and double-angle trigonometric functions. Encountered the first time last year, they were like a foreign language to the students. Some students may master them the first time they encounter them, but most do not. A second encounter with these trigonometric functions enables students to better understand them rather than struggling with them as they did the previous year.

As with the previous year in this textbook, students use two days per lesson, doing the odd numbered problems one day and the even numbered problems the second day. Again, students take a test every eight days. Since there are only one hundred twenty-five lessons in Advanced Mathematics, students will run out of textbook with about nine to ten weeks of school left.

Upon completing the entirety of Advanced Mathematics, students then pick up the first edition of Calculus and revert to doing a lesson a day and a test every Friday. They should complete at least through lesson twenty-seven (Introduction to Derivatives).

Students may elect to continue taking two days per lesson. Since these first twenty or so lessons are a lot like the material in the last few lessons of Advanced Mathematics, and they did not have a summer break between the two books, students may find they have already mastered the concepts and do not need the extra day.

The second year using Advanced Mathematics, the students receive a first semester credit for Trigonometry and a second semester credit for Precalculus. The following academic year they either proceed to a university or college or take Calculus their senior year in high school.

Geometry Credit

As John Saxon observed during his world travels, the United States is the only industrialized nation in the world that neatly packages its mathematics into separately titled courses like *Algebra, Geometry, Trigonometry,* etc.

If you were to meet international students coming to the United States as high school exchange students, you would notice they arrive with a single high school math textbook that contains algebra, geometry, trigonometry and calculus.

John Saxon wanted to integrate geometry concepts throughout his math books instead of isolating them in individual chapters or books as other publishing companies were doing. Interwoven in all of John Saxon's math books is introductory, basic, and advanced geometry depending upon the level of the book.

The actual geometry terms start as far back as *Math 54* in the hardback textbooks. But it is not until students reach *Algebra 2* that they encounter concepts normally found in high school geometry textbooks. The question then arises, "Is this formal or informal geometry?"

What that question is really asking is whether or not the students do formal two-column proofs. Without the formal two-column proofs, the old high school geometry teachers referred to the textbook material as *Informal Geometry.* With the formal two-column proofs, it was described as *Formal Geometry.*

In John Saxon's math books, students who complete the entirety of the second or third edition of *Algebra 2* have also completed the equivalent of the first semester of *Formal Geometry.* If parents would rather use another term, *Analytic Geometry* could be used.

While finishing the first half of *Advanced Mathematics,* the student completes the equivalent of the second semester of formal or *Analytic Geometry.* Students continue to do geometry problems and proofs throughout the remainder of the textbook, but no new geometry concepts are introduced.

Whenever I am asked what geometry title to put on the transcript, I tell parents to use just the title of *Geometry.* I cannot recall ever seeing a high school transcript that recorded *Formal Geometry, Informal Geometry, Analytic Geometry, non-Analytic Geometry, Euclidean Geometry, or non-Euclidean Geometry.* The transcript reflected just *Geometry.*

The advent of computer programming courses in high school has created a unique situation where the same skills encountered doing two-column geometry proofs can now be learned by taking a computer programming course.

The geometry learned through the first half of *Advanced Mathematics* is all that is needed to be successful in that area on the ACT or SAT tests. I see no reason to add another separate geometry course.

However, if parents desire that students take a separate geometry course, they should not place that course between *Algebra 1* and *Algebra 2.* During the time lapse, which could be as long as twelve to fifteen months, the average student will have forgotten many of the concepts encountered in *Algebra 1* necessary for success in *Algebra 2.*

Calculus

While generally referred to by its short title as *Calculus,* the textbook is officially titled *Calculus with Trigonometry and Analytic Geometry.* Both editions have the official title of *Calculus with Trigonometry and Analytic Geometry.* I shall just refer to them in the remainder of this chapter as *Calculus.*

There are now two homeschool editions of that book. They are the older first edition, which does not have lesson reference numbers or test solutions, and the newly released second edition, which has both features.

Students do not fail calculus because they cannot understand the calculus concepts. They fail calculus because they have a weak algebra background. So, regardless of which edition you choose, make sure the student has completed *Algebra 2,* as well as *Advanced Mathematics* or some other precalculus textbook, before attempting either edition of *Calculus.*

The older first edition of *Calculus* prepared students for the AB version of the Advanced Placement (AP) test. The contents of that edition did not fully prepare them for the entire BC version of the test.

The second edition of *Calculus* was released to provide students with the option of taking a calculus course that would prepare them for the BC version of the AP calculus test as well.

However, in order for students to be adequately prepared for the BC version of the test, they must complete all one hundred forty-eight lessons of the new second edition of *Calculus.* The BC content of the AP calculus test is contained in the last fifty lessons of the second edition of *Calculus.*

If students complete only the first ninety-eight lessons in the new second edition of *Calculus,* that portion would not adequately prepare them for the BC version of the AP calculus test.

The components of the first edition of *Calculus*, referred to by Saxon Publishers as the *Homeschool Kit,* included:

- A hardcover Student Textbook that contains answers to only the odd numbered problems.

- A softcover booklet titled Home Study Packet that contains answers to both the weekly tests and the even numbered problems in the daily assignments.

- A softcover booklet titled Test Forms that contains the testing schedule and the twenty-nine tests.

There was also a softcover solutions manual containing step-by-step solutions to every problem in the textbook. The solutions manual was sold separately. If parents want to buy a used copy of *Calculus*, they should make sure that that have all the pages and tests for each of the individual booklets.

The components of the new second edition of *Calculus* are still referred to as the *Homeschool Kit.* The components include:

- A hardcover student textbook that contains answers to only the odd numbered problems.

- A softcover booklet titled ***Answer Key*** that contains answers to all of the problems contained in the daily assignments.

- A stiff softcover booklet titled ***Homeschool Testing Book*** that contains the testing schedule and thirty-seven tests with step-by-step solutions to the test questions.

There is also a softcover solutions manual containing step-by-step solutions to every problem in the textbook. The solutions manual is sold separately.

The second edition of *Calculus*, which often references use of the graphing calculator, does not, however, teach students how to use their graphing calculators. Students should not attempt this textbook unless they have already mastered use of the graphing calculator.

If the purpose of students taking calculus is to learn calculus, then I recommend they use the first edition of the textbook along with their inexpensive scientific calculator.

If students are planning on pursuing a major in literature, music or the arts, successful completion of the first edition of *Calculus* is more than sufficient. Successful completion of the first edition *Calculus* will allow them to CLEP out of any mandatory freshman math course at their university or college.

If students are planning on pursuing a major in Mathematics or Engineering, I strongly recommend they plan on taking *Calculus I, II*, and *III* at their university or college regardless of which edition of *Calculus* they use. The first edition will, however, prepare them for these college calculus courses.

I would recommend high school calculus students not CLEP out of any of their college or university calculus courses, as they will now be able to sit back in class and listen to their professor discuss functions and their applications more clearly. This was not possible while learning the basics of calculus on their own at home.

As I have often told homeschool students, they could also make some easy money tutoring their struggling collegiate classmates.

Physics

The current edition of *Physics* is still the first edition which was initially published and released in July of 1993. It is an *Engineering Physics* book and not an *Introduction to Physics* or a *Basic or General Physics* textbook.

The textbook contains one hundred lessons. There are twenty-five regular tests, as well as four quarterly tests and a separate first and second semester exam. A comprehensive multiple choice final exam is also included in the test packet. The three components of the first edition of *Physics* are referred to as the *Homeschool Physics Kit.* The components of this kit include:

- A hardcover student textbook.

- A softcover booklet titled Home Study Packet that contains answers to both the tests and answers to all the problems in the daily assignments.

- A softcover booklet titled Test Forms that contains the testing schedule, thirty-five tests, four quarterly tests, and a final exam.

There is also a softcover solutions manual containing step-by-step solutions to every problem in the textbook. The solutions manual is sold separately. The textbook was designed as a full year's course for a regular nine-month school year.

Parents searching the school web site might have noticed the schools also have a *Laboratory Experiments Manual* that is not offered home school students. You can order one from the Saxon School Web site, but I do not believe you need one to learn physics.

Unless parents have the necessary, and I might add costly, lab equipment available to conduct the lab experiments, the lab manual is not needed to learn physics in high school. A scientific calculator is all the additional equipment needed for this course.

Students entering an engineering field would certainly want to take the college version of physics to include the associated laboratories. *Physics* is an excellent course for preparing future engineering students for that option.

Some parents are under the impression that *Physics* can be used by students who have mastered only the concepts of an algebra two textbook. This may work for a small select group of exceptionally strong math students, but not all students will do well in this book having completed only *Algebra 2*.

Because the book is an engineering physics textbook, I would not recommend students use this textbook until they have satisfactorily completed the first half of the second edition of *Advanced Mathematics* or some other precalculus textbook that contains trigonometry. The use of vectors requires a solid understanding of vectors from both algebra, as well as trigonometry.

The cumulative nature of the problems found in each lesson mirrors that of its math counterparts as do the tests. While there are quarterly, as well as semester final exams, the cumulative nature of the weekly tests can easily determine the mastery level of the student as was true in the math textbooks.

Transcription of Math Credits

I am not familiar with the legal requirements for maintaining transcripts for home school students in all of the fifty states; however, I can make several recommendations for recording course completions that will apply to any of them.

Just as the homeschool parent would not enter *Houghton Mifflin* fourth or fifth grade math on a student's transcript, there is also no reason to record *Saxon Math 54* or *Saxon Math 65* on a fourth or fifth grade transcript either. Recording fourth or fifth grade mathematics and the numerical or letter grade will suffice.

Since colleges rarely want to see elementary or middle school transcripts, what is recorded on the student's high school transcript is important to them. Again, just as one would not put *Harcourt Brace Algebra 1*, there is no need to record *Saxon Algebra 1* either. Just *Algebra 1* or *Algebra 2* and the associated numerical or letter grade will suffice.

Students who use the *Two Textbooks - Four Years* approach to completing *Algebra 1* and *Algebra 2*, would have their transcript reflect *Basic Algebra* their freshman year, *Algebra 1* their sophomore year, *Introduction to Algebra 2* their junior year, and *Algebra 2* their senior year along with their respective numerical or letter grades for the four years of high school mathematics.

Upon completion of *Algebra 2*, students will have also completed the equivalent of the first semester of a high school geometry course. They can also receive a semester credit for a high school geometry course if they do not continue into *Advanced Mathematics*. All that is needed on the transcript is the entry of *Geometry* and the same numerical or letter grade the student received in the second semester of *Algebra 2*.

Whether the student takes two, three or four semesters to complete *Advanced Mathematics*, do not record *Advanced Mathematics* on the student's transcript.

It became evident to me at the university where I taught that registrars and heads of math departments in colleges and universities do not like such titles. They want to see titles they are familiar with like *Algebra 1, Algebra 2, Trigonometry,* and *Geometry.* These are course titles they understand.

If the parent records *Advanced Mathematics* on the transcript, some college or university official will ask for a course description of the contents of that textbook. They cannot determine what is covered in the book by the title of *Advanced Mathematics.*

Because some institutions of higher learning do not always accept course titles on home school transcripts, they may still ask for a course description even though the transcript clearly reflects *Algebra 1, Algebra 2, Trigonometry,* etc.

If this occurs, one can simply make a copy of the table of contents at the front of the textbook and attach it to a paper titled *Course Descriptions* accompanying the transcript.

If the student satisfactorily completed the entirety of the second edition of *Advanced Mathematics* in a single year, completing all of the required problems and lessons in that textbook, then the following entries can be made on the student's transcript:

First Semester: Record a full credit titled either *Geometry or Geometry w/Advanced Algebra.* The other ½ credit from geometry was earned by the student when he satisfactorily completed *Algebra 2.*

Second Semester: Record a semester ½ credit for *Precalculus.*

110

Students who successfully complete the second edition of Saxon *Advanced Mathematics* in the recommended four semesters should have their high school transcript annotated with the following titles and credits:

First Semester: Record a semester ½ credit for high school *Geometry.*

Second Semester: Record a semester ½ credit for high school *Geometry.*

Third Semester: Record a semester ½ credit for *Trigonometry.*

Fourth Semester: Record a semester ½ credit for *Precalculus.*

Upon successful completion of John Saxon's math series from *Algebra 1* through *Advanced Mathematics*, the student's high school transcript should reflect a full credit each for *Algebra 1, Algebra 2,* and *Geometry* and a half credit each for *Trigonometry,* and *Precalculus.*

ACT and SAT Exams

Over the years, I have received hundreds of telephone calls from homeschool parents expressing concern about how John Saxon's math books may not prepare students for the ACT or SAT exams.

Taken at the right time, the books do an outstanding job of preparing students for either test. Most of my students attended colleges and universities in the Midwest so they took the ACT exam. The math content is about the same on both tests, but I am more familiar with the ACT results than the SAT.

Most of the students first took the ACT exam in the fall of their junior year while they were more than half-way through *Advanced Mathematics*, having completed the first ninety lessons the previous year as sophomores.

Their ACT math scores were generally in the high twenties, with some in the low thirties the first time they took the test. However, when they re-took the exam in the fall of their senior year they all received scores in the very high twenties or low thirties. Most of these students had already completed *Advanced Mathematics* and were now halfway through *Calculus*.

Quite a few of the scores were in the low to mid-thirties. I remember a few were just a point or two below the maximum of thirty-six. However, I had only one student max the math portion of the ACT exam. She was the National Merit Scholar I spoke about earlier in the book.

Students using John Saxon's math books should do just as well on the standardized SAT exams. However, they should not try to take them before they have completed at least the first half of the second edition of Advanced *Mathematics.*

I also have received numerous calls from homeschool parents concerned that the ACT and SAT geometry requirements are not adequately covered in John Saxon's math books. They had been advised to have the student take a regular geometry course also.

That would be true if they had the student attempting to take the ACT or SAT in the eighth grade, or in their freshman year of high school, just after completing *Algebra 1* or *Algebra 2*.

However, waiting until the student has successfully completed at least the first half of the second edition of *Advanced Mathematics* will resolve that problem. Remember also that the introduction of trigonometric functions is not completed until around lesson ninety in that textbook.

About the Author

Art Reed has more then twelve years of Saxon teaching experience at a rural high school in Enid, Oklahoma. Using John Saxon's math books, he taught high school mathematics from *Algebra ½* through *Calculus*. He was instrumental in raising the school's average math ACT scores from 13.4 to 21.9 in just four years. The school's scores were above the national average of 20.2 – and this was more than fifteen years ago!

Besides exceeding the national averages in math ACT scores, the high school also had more than ninety percent of their seniors taking math courses that were above algebra one. Additionally, the actual number of high school students taking the ACT tests had tripled!

Sometime later, while teaching mathematics at the local university, he asked for and received permission from the university to use John Saxon's *Algebra 2* textbook for the nontraditional students who were entering the university.

These students had failed the college's math entrance exam. They needed a non-credit algebra course that would allow them to review high school algebra so they could understand and pass the credited college algebra course the following year.

More than ninety percent of the adult students who enrolled in the non-credit *Algebra 2* courses received a grade of C or better. They successfully passed the university's credited algebra course their first time the following year.

While still teaching high school mathematics, Art was asked by Saxon Publishers to do the "Beta" testing for their early edition of their *Test Generating Software* for use in the classroom.

Art Reed retired from classroom teaching in 1999. Because of his hands-on experience and success with teaching from John Saxon's math books, he was asked to assume duties as the curriculum advisor in the Home School Division of Saxon Publishers, for the upper level math textbooks from *Math 76* through *Calculus* and *Physics.*

His experiences and depth of knowledge regarding John Saxon's math curriculum have enabled him to advise and assist parents and educators at all levels on how to successfully get the most from their Saxon textbooks and to ensure that their students received a quality education in mathematics.

During the past nine years, Art Reed has become well known for his sound curriculum advice to homeschool parents. He has come to be known as an experienced curriculum advisor for John Saxon's math textbooks from *Math 76* through *Calculus* and *Physics.* Homeschool parents using Saxon math textbooks have come to ask for him by name to seek his valued advice and assistance.

He has established the same professional reputation among school administrators and teachers for his assistance in helping them establish a quality Saxon math program within their school districts.

Art Reed was born in Chicago, Illinois, in 1936. He attended private Lutheran schools in Chicago through high school, graduating in 1954. In the fall of that same year, he enlisted in the United States Army. He spent more than twenty-seven years in the U.S. Army, both enlisted and commissioned service, retiring as a Lieutenant Colonel in 1981.

While on active duty, he served with the U.S. Army Special Forces, including two combat tours of duty with them in the Republic of Vietnam (1963 – 1965).

While assigned to the 5th Special Forces Group in Vietnam, he received the Bronze Star, the Purple Heart, and the Vietnamese Cross of Gallantry with palm. He also was awarded the Air Medal and the Combat Infantryman's Badge (CIB).

Among his other military decorations are the Soldiers Medal [awarded for heroism not involving direct contact with an armed enemy], the Legion of Merit, the Presidential Unit Citation, and the Meritorious Service Medal. He is a Master Parachutist with more than 200 parachute jumps.

Art Reed's non-combat military assignments included duties in the U.S. Army Research Office, Office of the Chief of Research and Development, the Office of the Army Chief of Staff, and the Congressional Liaison Office in Washington, D.C.

He is a qualified nuclear weapons officer, as well as an engineer and mathematician, receiving his Bachelor of Science degree from Oklahoma State University, and later earning a second degree in mathematics from Phillips University.

Art and his wife Judy have been married for more than forty years. They reside in Enid, Oklahoma, as do their two daughters and their families, which include five grandchildren.